CONDUCTORS AND SEMICONDUCTORS

CONDUCTORS AND SEMICONDUCTORS

By **ALAN HOLDEN**

BELL TELEPHONE LABORATORIES

Library of Congress Catalog Number 64-7541

Composed, printed, and bound by
Edward Stern & Company, Philadelphia, Pa.

Portrait of Niels Bohr courtesy *Physics Today*; that of
F. W. Kohlrausch courtesy Freie Universität Berlin;
that of Paul Drude from Deutsches Museum, Munich.
All other portraits from The Bettman Archive, New York.

The Bell System Aid to High School Science Program

■ A classroom demonstration device that schools may purchase to show various properties of conductors and semiconductors is described on page 130 of this book.

■ A manual, "Experiments with Conductors and Semiconductors," which students may use in the school laboratory, can also be obtained from local Telephone Business Offices.

■ Any of the main illustrations in this book (Figures 1 through 48) is available as a transparency for use in overhead projectors. These may be obtained from:

    Jack Steinberg Studios, Inc.
    230 Park Avenue
    New York, N. Y. 10017
    Price: $3.00 each

■ Additional copies of this book may be obtained in limited quantities from local Telephone Business Offices or purchased from the distributor:

    Edward Stern & Company
    Independence Mall
    Philadelphia, Pa. 19105
    Prices: $ .65 each (paperbound)
           $1.20 each (hard cover)

■ Information about other items in the Bell System Aid to High School Science Program is also available from local Telephone Business Offices:

Classroom units (books, films, demonstration devices):
    Similarities in Wave Behavior
    Ferromagnetic Domains
    The Speech Chain

Bell System Science Experiments:
    From Sun to Sound
    Solar Energy Experiment
    Speech Synthesis
    Experiments with Crystals and Light

"Find me a way" an ancient despot might have said "to send invisible messages round the world, and I will ennoble and enrich you." The reward would never have been won. "Find out," he might less plausibly have said, "about the strange force in this little piece of amber." This apparent frivolity contained the secret of his first requirement, but remote and unforeseeable.

From the address of Sir Cyril Hinshelwood on the Tercentenary of the Royal Society, 1960.

Table of Contents

vii

Foreword

Scientific knowledge is *knowledge*, not fact—a gallery of pictures painted by men to portray in some simplified, comprehensible way the seemingly infinite complexity of nature. The pictures are put up and taken down, cleaned, replaced, and destroyed. Any account of scientific knowledge is therefore a "progress report"—an account of unfinished business.

Those who transact that business come and go with birth and death, prosper when they are paid, suffer when they are neglected. The fortunes of the business rise and fall with theirs. We cannot know what science would look like if Sir Isaac Newton had not been distracted into becoming Warden of the Mint— or if Henry Moseley had not been sent to an early death in World War I. And like other human activities, science has its fashions, set by powerful stylists such as Niels Bohr and Albert Einstein.

The following account tells a little of the story of electrical conduction through solid materials, from Stephen Gray's "packthread" to the transistor of our time. In tracing this story, you must expect to take some rather long excursions away from its main course—into the nature of atomic structure, the behavior of gases, the ways that atoms are arranged in crystals, and the like. These matters, seemingly so remote from electrical conduction, turn out to bear on it closely. Indeed, in the eyes of those who have made them, all these pictures are only fragments of a single picture. It is a picture of nature that is always incomplete, but must always hang together with the consistency contributed by the single palette used in painting it: the mind of man.

1 Conductors and Nonconductors

Unlike the goddess Athena, who sprang full-grown from the head of Zeus, today's scientific knowledge was slowly made by men. A few were of towering intellect and many more were of modest attainment, but all were itched by the desire to get an account of the way things are. Without doubt that activity, continuing to this day, will continue through the foreseeable future. The leisure to pursue it grows with the increasing well-being of mankind; and the pursuit yields rewards in further increasing man's well-being. If you would make science yourself, you would do well to study how others have made it — to put yourself into the past a little — to wonder whether you would have done as well.

Early Experiments with Conduction

In the Eighteenth Century Stephen Gray, who had heard that glass could be electrified by rubbing it, noticed that an ivory ball, attached by a stick to a cork in the end of a glass tube, picked up electrification from the tube. "This put me upon thinking," he wrote, "whether if the ball were hung by a pack-thread and suspended by a loop on the tube, the electricity would not be carried down the line to the ball: accordingly, upon suspending the ball on the tube by a pack-thread about three foot long, when the tube had been excited by rubbing, the ivory ball attracted and repelled the leaf-brass over which it was held, as freely as it had done when it was suspended on sticks or wire."

Gray then tried to carry the electricity a longer distance, through pack-thread (a coarse fiber made from hemp) looped over nails in the beams of his house. He did not succeed, and guessed that the electricity might be carried downwards but not horizontally. How far downwards? To find out, he conducted experiments in the cupola of St. Paul's in London, with the help of his friend Granville Wheeler.

At St. Paul's Gray was able to increase the vertical length of his pack-thread lines. "The first was from the window in the

1

long gallery that opened into the hall, about sixteen foot high; the next from the battlements of the house down into the fore court, twenty-nine foot; then from the clock turret to the ground, which was thirty-four foot, this being the greatest height we could come at . . . the leaf-brass was attracted and repelled beyond what I expected."

But when Wheeler suggested that experiments could be carried out over longer distances if the pack-thread were arranged horizontally, Gray remembered his failure to accomplish horizontal transmission in his house. The two men decided that perhaps the "electrical effluvia" were being shared between Gray's nails and his pack-thread; and since the nails were much thicker than the pack-thread, they might carry away most of the electricity. Wheeler suggested that they support the line with threads made from fine silk, which was much thinner than the pack-thread. This might leave more of the electricity in the line. And so it did. In successive experiments, doubling their line back and forth in a barn, Gray and Wheeler succeeded in transmitting the electricity 293 feet.

When they lengthened their line by still another pass, the silk thread broke. Searching for a stronger suspension, but one that would still be thin compared with the pack-thread, the two men tried some fine brass wire. But now their pack-thread line, suspended from the wire, would no longer transmit the electricity to its distant end.

"By this we were now convinced that our former success depended upon the lines that supported the line of communication being silk, and not upon their being small, as before the trial I imagined; the same effect happening here as when the line that is to convey the electric virtue is supported by pack-thread; viz., that when the effluvia come to the wires or pack-thread that support the line, they pass by them to the timber to which each end of them is fixed, and so go no further forward in the line that is to carry them to the ivory ball."

In this way Stephen Gray was the first to report discovery of the difference between electric conductors and nonconductors.

Gray's report will bring a glow of recognition to any experimental scientist. He too has started with an unexpected observation—that the ivory ball picks up electricity from the electrified glass. He too has pushed that observation a step further—that the electricity will go down through pack-thread. Like Gray, he has perhaps guessed wrong—that electricity tumbles downward as water would, and will not flow horizontally. Not content with just one guess, he has come up with another possible explanation of his failure—that his means of suspension might be too big. And, pursuing that alternative, he too has discovered that the true fact is other than any he had imagined.

Mr. Gray's pack-thread was made of hemp, a strong vegetable fiber. His experiments suggest that hemp would be a poor material to use for electrical insulation—that silk, the animal fiber spun by silkworms, would be much better. Is it generally true that animal fibers are better insulators than vegetable fibers? Perhaps you would be interested to pursue this question by using Gray's method, trying also such animal fibers as wool, such vegetable fibers as cotton, and such synthetic fibers as nylon, in the way described in Figure 1.

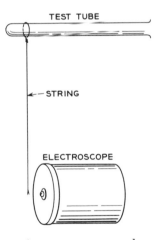

FIGURE 1 – STEPHEN GRAY'S EXPERIMENT *can be repeated conveniently by tying a string around one end of a glass test-tube, rubbing the test-tube vigorously with one hand, and touching the other end of the string to an electroscope.*

Clearly Gray's experimental method will at best give you only a qualitative answer: It cannot tell you *how much* one fiber is better or worse than another. Indeed, using the knowledge of his time, Gray could not put numbers into his answers. The numbers awaited a century and a half of patient experimenting, interpreting, and checking by others, and the formulation of quantitative ways for describing electrical behavior.

What Is Electricity?

Early in this work it became clear that electricity is a quite unusual substance. Surely it is "fluid": It will flow from place to place. But apparently it is also what has been called an "impalpable fluid": When it is transferred from one body to

---

STEPHEN GRAY (1696-1736) *was probably born in Canterbury, England, although almost nothing is known of his early life. At any rate, he was living on his estate at Canterbury when, like many eighteenth-century English country gentlemen, he became interested in the study of "natural philosophy." Gray set up his own home astronomical observatory, studied microscopy, and invented an unusual microscope that used a tiny drop of water as a lens. But it was Gray's pioneering investigations of electrical conductors and insulators that led many people to call him "The Father of Electrical Science." In the latter part of his short life Gray took up residence in the ancient Charterhouse School in London, where he devoted himself to full-time research into electrical phenomena. In 1732 he was elected a Fellow of the Royal Society, whose* Philosophical Transactions *published Gray's letters describing his research, including the excerpt on pages 1 and 2 of this book.*

Gray's early experiments followed those of William Gilbert, Robert Boyle, and others and convinced him that substances could be classified into two groups: those, such as hair, feathers, or glass, that could be "electrified" by rubbing—which Gray called "electrics"—and those that could not be, which he called "non-electrics." (These latter, of course, are actually the electrical conductors.) We have quoted Gray's own story of his ingenious attempts to conduct electricity along packthread strung across St. Paul's in London and at the country estate of his friend Sir Granville Wheeler. Gray performed very early experiments with electrical luminescence, the storage of electricity (long before the invention of the Leyden jar), and electrostatic induction. He also suggested, several decades before Benjamin Franklin confirmed it, that the tiny electrical sparks that man could produce were actually identical to the awesome electrical power seen in lightning.

What most led to Gray's fame among his contemporaries were his tests to show that the human body could be an electrical conductor. Although he was not daring enough to test this then-revolutionary idea on his own body, Gray did employ that of his footboy—"a good stout lad of nine years." After suspending this lucky chap in the air from strong silk lines, Gray began rubbing a three-foot glass tube to generate "electric virtue." Sure enough, when the electrified tube was held next to the boy's feet, a piece of leaf brass set up on a stand a few inches below the boy's face began to twitch. This unprecedented phenomenon produced much interested speculation in scientific circles, but the unlearned made wild guesses about Stephen Gray's compact with the Evil One.

another, it seems never to diminish or increase the weight of either by a noticeable amount.

Perhaps there are even "two distinct electricities, very different from one another." The early Eighteenth Century French chemist Charles Dufay distinguished the "vitreous electricity" in rubbed glass from the "resinous electricity" in rubbed amber. When they were electrified, glass would repel glass, and amber would repel amber, but glass would attract amber. "In order to know immediately, to which of the two classes of electricity belongs any body whatsoever, one need only render electrical a silk thread, which is known to be of the *resinous electricity*, and see whether that body, rendered electrical, attracts or repels it. If it attracts, it is certainly of that kind of electricity which I call *vitreous*; if on the contrary it repels, it is of the same kind of electricity with the silk, that is, of the *resinous*. I have likewise observed that communicated electricity retains the same properties."

Benjamin Franklin, however, preferred to explain such effects by a one-fluid, not a two-fluid, theory. Observing the sparks that may fly from one electrified body to another, he concluded that "electrical fire is a common element." From bodies that have acquired more than their share, the fluid will pass to others that have less. "And we daily in our experiments electrise plus or minus, as we think proper."

Modern Idea of Electricity

Today we use Dufay's idea and Franklin's language: We recognize "positively charged" and "negatively charged" objects. In our minds we subdivide those objects into atomic constituents, and then divide the atoms into still smaller constituents. Those electrons and nuclei, of which we imagine matter to be made, are all the bearers of electrical charges; the electrons are charged negatively, the nuclei positively. What *are* the charges that these tiny particles bear? We do not know; we can say only that the electrical charges are properties of the particles, as their masses are.

In this picture of matter, you can see the preservation of Dufay's idea: There are two kinds of electricity, positive and negative. You can see also the suitability of Franklin's language: Positive electricity and negative electricity cancel each other in their combined effects. Every piece of matter contains large amounts of both electricities, but from outside they appear to contain only the net amount—the difference between one kind and the other. And now the word "amount" has slipped

---

BENJAMIN FRANKLIN (1706-1790) *is often described as an "American diplomat, statesman, and scientist," but he preferred to describe himself as "Benjamin Franklin, Printer." In fact he printed and published the first novel to appear in America, established presses from New Haven, Connecticut, to Kingston, Jamaica, and late in life had a private press in his house in Passy, France.*

FRANKLIN

It is impossible to summarize the versatile genius of this extraordinary man. His writings on economics, though undertaken for a political purpose, rank him as America's first economist. His "Autobiography" gives him an immortal place in literature. He formed the first police force in the colonies, and the first fire company. Over ten years he organized the American postal service into an efficient and financially successful enterprise. By the time he was 56 years old he had received the freedom of the city of Edinburgh, Scotland, and the degrees of doctor of laws from the University of St. Andrews, of master of arts from Harvard, Yale, and the College of William and Mary, and the D.C.L. from Oxford. Before he died he had been elected to the Royal Academy of Sciences and the Royal Medical Academy of Paris, and to the Royal Society and the Medical Society of London.

Franklin always hoped to retire from public life and devote himself to science, but the strenuous times in which he lived continually called him into new political and diplomatic activity. At the age of 70 he found himself taking off for France to conduct the diplomatic relations of the rebellious American colonies there, and later to negotiate the peace with Britain. Meanwhile he had written papers on waterspouts and whirlwinds and the causes of earthquakes, invented the "Franklin stove" and means for abating the smoke of chimneys and street lamps, performed his famous kite experiment, studied the temperature of the Gulf Stream, experimented with oil on stormy waters, and invented bifocal eyeglasses for his own use.

The historian Henri Martin speaks of Franklin as "of a mind altogether French in its grace and elasticity," thus according him the highest praise that a Frenchman knows. The novelist Honoré de Balzac said that he "invented the lightning-rod, the hoax, and the republic." One of his cleverest hoaxes was "An Edict of the King of Prussia" in 1773, proclaiming on numerous substantial grounds that Britain was a colony of Prussia and should therefore submit to certain taxes—identical with those then levied by Britain on the American colonies.

inevitably into our speech. How can we measure the *amount* of electricity—the net amount that an object has?

A clue to measurement can be drawn from Dufay's observation that electrically charged objects attract and repel one another. Attractions and repulsions are *forces*. Since we have a way for measuring the amount of a force, we should be able to measure the amount of an electrical charge in terms of the force that the charge will exert.

Coulomb Investigates Force

Near the end of the Eighteenth Century, Charles-Augustin Coulomb found a way to pursue this clue. He had already invented the torsion balance, shown diagrammatically in Figure 2,

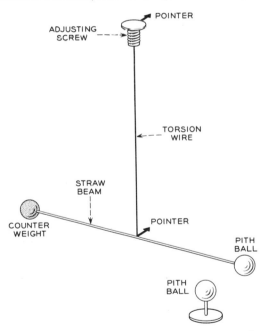

FIGURE 2 – COULOMB'S TORSION BALANCE *enabled him to discover the law governing the force between two electrically charged spheres.*

and had found that the angle through which a force will twist a wire is directly proportional to the twisting force. In 1785 he went on to make a brilliant application of his balance to the study of the force between two electrically charged bodies.

Coulomb suspended a light straw beam, with a pith ball at one end and a paper counterweight at the other, on a fine silver wire. He put another similar pith ball in a fixed position, just touching the ball on the straw beam. Then he charged the head of a pin, and touched it to the two pith balls. Instantly the pinhead shared its charge with the pith balls, and the electrical repulsion between the balls made the ball on the balance leap away from the fixed ball — until the repulsive force between them was counterbalanced by the twist in the suspending wire.

Thus the angle through which the wire was twisted could provide a number proportional to the repulsive force between the two balls at that distance from each other. By turning the screw that held the upper end of the wire, Coulomb could turn the wire at will, and so increase or reduce the force that balanced the repulsive force. Accordingly the balls would approach or recede from each other. In this way he could get numbers — the angles — proportional to the force between the balls at different separations. After many such experiments he was able to announce that "the repulsive force between two small spheres,

---

CHARLES-AUGUSTIN COULOMB (1736-1806) *was born at Angoulême, France. After studying in Paris, he joined the army as an officer of engineers, and was sent to Martinique. Service in the West Indies so impaired his health that he returned to France, accepting in succession posts at Rochelle, the Isle of Aix, and Cherbourg. In 1781 he received a permanent assignment in Paris, but he resigned from it at the outbreak of the revolution and retired to a small estate at Blois to devote himself to scientific research.*

COULOMB

Before that, he had designed the torsion balance described in Figure 2, without realizing that the Rev. John Michell in England had already designed a somewhat similar balance, soon to be used by Henry Cavendish for making direct measurements of gravitational forces. Coulomb first used his balance to measure the torsional elasticity of metal and silk fibers, and then went on to measure the forces exerted by electrical charges, as described on pages 7-8, not only when the forces were repulsive but also when they were attractive. He believed in the "two-fluid" theory of both electricity and magnetism, and he verified the inverse-square law of force for "magnetic particles" also. But he recognized clearly that, whereas the two "electric fluids" were separable, the two "magnetic fluids" were not. He also stated that, in all these cases of action at a distance, the intervening medium played no part.

charged with the same sort of electricity, is in the inverse ratio of the squares of the distances between the centers of the two spheres."

Measuring the Quantity of Charge

Coulomb's announcement left the *amount* of charge still unmeasured; it spoke only of how the force between any pair of charged spheres varies with their distance apart. Other investigators went on to study the effect of changing the charges on the spheres. It is useful to imagine today how Coulomb himself might have done those studies with his own torsion balance.

For example, he might have prepared a third pith ball that was as nearly as possible identical with the ball on the beam. After making measurements with the ball on the beam, he might have touched it lightly and briefly with the third ball. During that contact the ball on the beam would share its charge with the third ball—equally, because the balls were identical. Then he could do the same experiment again, with some confidence that the ball on the beam retained just one half of its original charge.

In this way, changing the charge on the movable ball by known fractions, Coulomb would have found that the force was directly proportional to the charge on that ball. In other words, he could have written $F \sim q$, where F is the repulsive force between the balls, q is the charge on the movable ball, and the symbol $\sim$ means "varies with" or "is proportional to." Indeed, combining this result with his earlier result, he could have written $F \sim q/r^2$, where r is the distance between the fixed ball and the movable ball.

So far, Coulomb's results would speak only of the charge on the movable ball, assuming that the charge on the fixed ball stays the same. But the symmetry of his experiment would permit him to argue that the force must also be proportional to the charge on the fixed ball if the charge on the movable ball stays the same. Hence, if both the charges could change, the force would be proportional to the product of the two charges. Coulomb could have written $F \sim q_1 q_2/r^2$. That way of writing would be a summary of the statement, "The force between sphere #1 and sphere #2 is directly proportional to the charge on each sphere and inversely proportional to the square of the distance between them."

Such statements as these still avoid the issue of putting a number to an amount of charge. But the last statement suggests a way for *defining* such a number. Let us call the charge "one unit" if two spheres with that amount of charge repel each other with a force of one *dyne* when they are one centimeter apart. Then the symbol $\sim$ can be replaced by the symbol $=$, and Coulomb's law can be written $F = q_1q_2/r^2$. That choice of the unit of charge forms the foundation of the electrostatic system of electrical units; it is called the *statcoulomb*.

Volta's Pile

Thus by the opening of the Nineteenth Century Gray, Dufay, Franklin, and Coulomb had succeeded in establishing many of the properties of electricity. In particular, bodies possessing excesses of one or the other kind of electricity would exert forces on one another; and those excesses would flow from one body to another through a variety of conducting materials. Then, in 1800, Alessandro Volta invented the "pile" (Figure 3) with which his name is still associated, "which in a word provides an unlimited charge or imposes a perpetual action or impulsion on the electric fluid." By making available continuous flows of electricity, Volta provided the final means required to

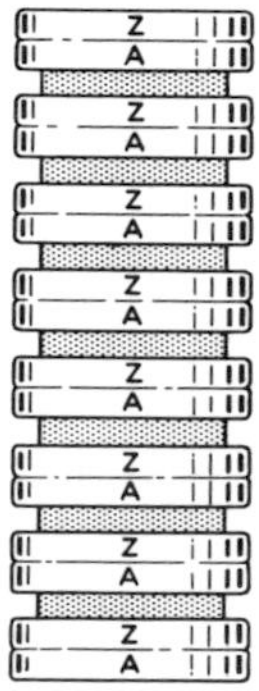

FIGURE 3 – VOLTA'S PILE *was described by Volta himself thus: "I place horizontally on a table or base one of the metallic plates, for example, one of the silver ones, and on this first plate I place a second plate of zinc; on this second plate I lay one of the moistened discs (of cardboard or leather); then another plate of silver followed immediately by another of zinc, on which I place again a moistened disc. I thus continue in the same way coupling a plate of silver with one of zinc, always in the same sense, that is to say, always silver below and zinc above or vice versa, according as I began, and inserting between these couples a moistened disc; I continue, I say, to form from several of these steps a column as high as can hold itself up without falling."*

develop a quantitative description of electrical behavior. In succeeding years that description was perfected into a form that can be summarized as follows:

Since charged bodies exert forces on one another, work can be derived by allowing those forces to move the bodies. If all the bodies except one "test body" were held fixed, the test body could do a definite amount of work by moving from one point to another. That amount of work measures the difference between the potential energies of the body when it occupies its

VOLTA

ALESSANDRO VOLTA (1745-1827) is primarily remembered for his invention of the voltaic pile and the common unit of electrical potential difference, the "volt," keeps his name alive. He was born at Como; he taught physics there and later at Pavia, and finally the emperor of Austria appointed him director of the philosophical faculty at Padua.

Volta developed his pile under the stimulus of the historic observations by his compatriot, Galvani, on the muscular spasms of freshly killed frogs in the presence of static electric charges. But the pile was more than a happy accident; it represented the culmination of study and insight in combination. Studying the conduction of electricity by liquids and solids, Volta was first led to put all electrical conductors into two classes, the first comprising primarily metals, and the second primarily electrolytic solutions. Examining them with an electroscope, he showed that two different conductors of the first class would acquire electric charges when they were simply touched to each other. He showed further that, if a series of discs of metal are placed in contact, the electrical potential difference between the first and the last in the series is the same as it is when those two are in immediate contact, with no intervening discs.

But if pairs of metallic discs are separated by discs of cloth wetted with a conductor of the second class, the potential differences between each pair become additive, giving a large potential difference when many pairs are stacked up in this way. Volta described the resulting "piles" in a letter to the president of the Royal Society of London in 1800. They were immediately put to use by many investigators; in the following year Napoleon called Volta to Paris to demonstrate his experiments, and ordered that a medal be struck in his honor.

Volta went on to examine all the metals available to him in pairs, in order to find out which became positively and which negatively charged. He was finally able to list the metals in an electromotive series, such that each metal becomes positive when placed in contact with the metal next below it in the series.

initial position and its final position. Of course the work depends on what those two positions are, and it is also directly proportional to the charge on the test body. Then, upon dividing that work by the amount of the charge, one can obtain a number that depends only on the two positions: It is the work done per unit of charge by any charged body that moves from one position to the other.

That number is called the *potential difference* between the two positions. If the work is measured in ergs and the charge in statcoulombs, the potential difference is measured in ergs per statcoulomb, called *statvolts*. It is important to recognize the relation between the electrostatic units of charge and potential difference, and the more familiar "practical" units. The practical unit of charge, the *coulomb*, is equal to 3×10^9 statcoulombs. The practical unit of work and energy, the *joule*, is equal to 10^7 ergs. Hence the practical unit of potential difference, the *volt*, which is one joule per coulomb, is equal to 1/300 statvolt.

A Measure for Current

We can now put a number to the "impulsion on the electric fluid" provided by such a device as Volta's pile: We say that there is a potential difference between its two ends, measurable in volts. When those two ends are connected together by something outside the pile, the "unlimited charge" will flow steadily through the connecting link under that impulsion. The flow of charge constitutes a current, whose magnitude is described by the amount of charge that flows through any cross-section of the connection in one unit of time. When charge is measured in coulombs and time in seconds, the current is measured in *amperes*. In other words, when a current of one ampere is flowing through such a connection, one coulomb of charge is passing in each second through any cross-section of the connection.

Obviously, the amount of current which passes through such a connection depends on how long and how thick the connection is, as well as the potential difference between its ends and the material of which it is made. With a single material and a single potential difference, you can easily guess how the current should depend on the length and the thickness of the connection. Surely the current should increase directly with the cross-section of the connection, because the cross-section measures the area through which the electric fluid must flow. And surely the current should vary inversely with the length of the connection, because each part of the electric fluid must push the part directly ahead of it through whatever resistance the connection offers. Experiments will readily check this reasoning.

Ohm's Law

To find out how the current through a connection varies with the potential difference that drives it, George Ohm undertook a series of experiments about 1825. Ohm had difficulty finding sources of current whose potential difference and delivery of charge did not fluctuate while he used them. Finally, he was able to show that the current through a connecting wire of brass or copper was directly proportional to the potential difference between the two ends of the connection.

Experiments such as Ohm's have since been extended to a wide variety of materials, and to a very much wider range of potential differences than he could command. Ohm's Law—the rule that the electric current through an electrical connection is directly proportional to the potential difference between its ends—appears to be obeyed quite generally so long as the connection does not contain junctions between

OHM

GEORG SIMON OHM (1787-1854) *pursued a career in mathematics and physics that had no great distinction except for the single piece of work referred to on this page, which he described in a pamphlet published in Berlin in 1827 and which is now summarized as "Ohm's Law." Ohm was born and educated in Erlangen. In 1817 he became professor of mathematics in the Jesuits' College at Cologne, and it was there that he wrote his memorable pamphlet.*

Strangely enough, the pamphlet was coldly received, and Ohm's feelings were so hurt by its neglect that he resigned his post and lived in poverty for six years until he was given a professorship at Nuremberg. Then his work began to be recognized, and in 1841 he was awarded the Copley Medal of the Royal Society. He spent the latter part of his life as conservator of the physical collection at Munich, and wrote a Text Book of Physics which was published in the same year that saw his death by apoplexy.

different materials. For conduction by metals the rule is especially reliable; in silver and gold, deviations of as much as one per cent from the rule have been observed only at the enormous current density of five million amperes per square centimeter. The rule is usually written $V = RI$, where V is the potential difference, I is the current, and R, the constant of proportionality, is called the *resistance* of the connection. When the potential difference is measured in volts and the current in amperes, the units of resistance are called *ohms*.

Electrical Properties of Material

But the most interesting questions arise from examining the large differences in the current that will flow through connections made of different materials, even when the size and shape of the connection, and the potential difference between its ends, are kept the same. Clearly the electric fluid must be contending with a very different environment in copper, through which the fluid flows readily, and glass through which it hardly flows at all. Putting numbers to such differences requires some method of quantitative description that is independent of the size and shape of any particular sample and refers only to the material of which it is made. Such a number is called a "property of the material."

The appropriate reasoning, leading to the definition of the required property, is described in the caption of Figure 4. The *conductivity*, or alternatively the *resistivity*, of a material is a number "attached to the material," so to speak. It can be found only by measuring the resistance of *some* sample of the material. But once it has been determined, the resistance offered by *any* connection made of that material can be calculated from the resistivity of the material and the size and shape of the connection.

It turns out that solid materials display an enormous range of resistivities at ordinary temperatures. The good electrical conductors — the metals — have resistivities of the order of 10^{-6} ohm-centimeter. "Insulating" materials such as glass have resistivities ranging up to 10^{17} ohm-centimeters. No wonder the electrical fluid passing through Gray's pack-thread line would leak away when he suspended the line from brass wire, and would stay in the line when he made his suspension of silk!

Probably it would be possible to find or make a material whose resistivity lies anywhere in this enormous range. But most materials fall in one or another of three classes at room

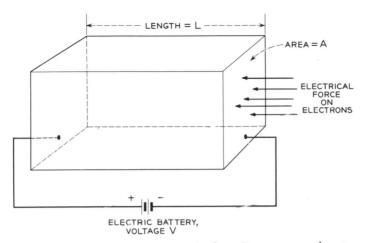

LENGTH = L

AREA = A

ELECTRICAL
FORCE
ON
ELECTRONS

+ ‖ −

ELECTRIC BATTERY,
VOLTAGE V

FIGURE 4 – AN ELECTRIC BATTERY, *of voltage* V, *is connected to two electrodes at opposite ends of a solid sample of length* L *and cross-sectional area* A. *The electrical force per unit charge* E *that the battery puts on any electrical charges in the sample is* V/L, *on the average. The current* I *carried by such charges is directly proportional to the number of parallel paths through which the current can flow – in other words, to the cross-sectional area* A *– and is inversely proportional to the length over which the charges are meeting resistance – in other words to the length* L. *Observing that the current is proportional to the voltage, you can write* I = GV, *where* G *is the "conductance" of the sample. From the above reasoning,* G = (A/L)g, *where* g *depends on the nature of the solid material and is called its* conductivity.

The statement that the current is proportional to the voltage can be turned around to read V = RI, *where* R *is the resistance of the sample. If* V *is measured in volts and* I *in amperes, the units of* R *are volts per ampere, and are usually called* ohms. *Since* R = I/G, *and* G = (A/L)g, *you can write* R = (L/A)·(1/g). *If you now introduce a new quantity* r, *defined by* r = 1/g, *you can rewrite the last expression as* R = (L/A)r. *Since* g *is a property of the solid substance, independent of the shape of the sample, so is* r; *it is called the* resistivity *of the material. Most people think that a property of a material is always reckoned per unit amount of the material. The density of a material, for example, is reckoned in grams per cubic centimeter. But it would be meaningless to reckon the resistivity in "ohms per cubic centimeter." Since* r = (A/L)R, *and* R *is reckoned in ohms,* L *in centimeters, and* A *in square centimeters, the units appropriate to the resistivity of a substance are* ohm-centimeters.

temperature: the good conductors (about 10^{-6} ohm-centimeter), the insulators (10^{14} to 10^{17} ohm-centimeters), and the semiconductors (10^{-2} to 10^9 ohm-centimeters). In our century pictures of the mechanism of electrical conduction in all these materials have been constructed to explain their behavior. Using these pictures, scientists and engineers are now able to "design" materials with predictable properties, and to make useful devices with their aid. The rest of this book is largely devoted to describing these pictures and how they lead to the design of such devices as the solar cell and the transistor.

2 The Nature of Electrical Current

Speaking of positively and negatively charged objects in the last chapter, we have already mentioned today's picture of matter. We believe that matter of any sort — solid, liquid, or gaseous — can be subdivided, in principle, into molecules, and those molecules into atoms. The atoms (and most molecules also) are invisibly tiny: One cubic inch of a solid contains about a million million million million atoms. Since they are too small to be seen with the most powerful microscope, the notion that matter is made in that way is hypothetical. But a mountain of indirect chemical and physical evidence, of very diverse kinds, has been accumulated to support that atomic hypothesis.

During the latter half of the Eighteenth Century there arose a similar "atomic" hypothesis regarding the impalpable electric fluid. In the middle of that century John Canton had discovered electrostatic induction. One electrified body produces charges upon another insulated body without touching it. If a person briefly touches this latter body while the inducing body is still near, the second body retains a charge of opposite sign to that of the inducing body.

The Atomic Theory of Electricity

Such observations, and many others, could be fitted well into a picture of a neutral electric fluid, which is made of little scraps of positive and negative electricity in numbers just sufficient to neutralize each other, and is possessed by all pieces of matter. It was natural to imagine that Dufay's observations on larger bodies would extend to these little units: Two like charges would repel each other and two unlike charges would attract. Then in Canton's experiment, for example, a positively charged body would induce charges in a neutral body by driving the positively charged ingredients of its electric fluid to its farther side and attracting the negatively charged ingredients to

16

Sir Humphry Davy (1778-1829) *was born at Penzance in Cornwall. His father died when he was 16 years old, and as the eldest of five children he undertook responsibility for them and his mother, leaving school to become apprentice to a surgeon-apothecary. Preparing for a career in medicine, he mapped out and pursued a remarkably broad course of self-instruction in metaphysics, ethics, mathematics and chemistry.*

DAVY

At about the age of 19 he became acquainted with Gregory Watt (a son of James Watt, inventor of the modern steam engine) and Davies Giddy (later president of the Royal Society), and at the instance of Giddy he was installed as superintendent of the Medical Pneumatic Institute, established in Bristol by Dr. Thomas Beddoes for investigating the medicinal properties of gases. He brought the institute into prominence by his discovery that pure nitrous oxide ("laughing gas") is respirable. It soon became fashionable in England to inhale the gas, and the poets Robert Southey and Samuel Coleridge were among the distinguished people who used to amuse themselves in that way.

In 1801 Count Rumford engaged Davy as assistant lecturer in chemistry and director of the laboratory at the Royal Institution in London, and appointed him professor the following year. He interested himself first in the chemistry of tanning, then in agricultural chemistry, but increasingly he became devoted to electrochemical researches, using the Royal Institution's unusually large battery.

Davy's first Bakerian lecture in 1806 to the Royal Society, "On Some Chemical Agencies of Electricity," was described by J. J. Berzelius as one of the most remarkable memoirs in chemical history. In his own summary: "Hydrogen, the alkaline substances, the metals, and certain metallic oxides are attracted by negatively electrified metallic surfaces, and repelled by positively electrified metallic surfaces; and contrariwise, oxygen and acid substances are attracted by positively electrified metallic surfaces and repelled by negatively electrified metallic surfaces; and these attractive and repulsive forces are sufficiently energetic to destroy or suspend the usual operation of elective affinity."

In 1813 Davy began a tour of Europe with his wife and young Michael Faraday, who had just been engaged as his laboratory assistant at the Royal Institution. With his scientific reputation at its zenith, he was accorded many honors and given every privilege. In Paris he examined the newly discovered substance, iodine, with his portable chemical laboratory, and soon pronounced it "an undecompoundable body," or in other words an element. In Genoa he investigated the electricity of the torpedo-fish. In Florence, with the aid of a great burning-glass in the Accademia del Cimento, he burned a diamond in oxygen and decided that it consisted of pure carbon. In Rome he inquired into the composition of ancient coloring materials.

its nearer side. Touching it would permit the positively charged units to flow still farther away under the repulsion of the inducing body, leaving a net negative charge when the contact was broken.

The appearance of Volta's pile in 1800 (Figure 3) quickly led to a series of electrochemical observations that had a pro-

---

MICHAEL FARADAY (1791-1867) *was the son of a blacksmith who had come to London from Yorkshire. As a boy he was apprenticed to a bookbinder, but he became interested while he was still quite young in the experimental study of nature. When he was 21 a customer of his master took him to hear four lectures delivered by Sir Humphry Davy at the Royal Institution. Faraday took notes on them, wrote them out in fuller form and, encouraged by his host, sent them to Sir Humphry. A year later he was appointed*

FARADAY

assistant in the laboratory of the Royal Institution, and soon accompanied Sir Humphry on a two-year tour of Europe.

Returned to London, he undertook chemical researches as assistant to Davy. He made a special study of chlorine and its chemical combinations. He did the first rough experiments on the diffusion of gases; he liquified several gases; he studied alloys of steel and made new kinds of optical glass. But from the outset his major interests were in the phenomena of electricity and magnetism, and here he made contributions of outstanding importance.

In 1831 Faraday made his crowning discovery, of the induction of an electric current in a wire by current in another wire, and by a magnet. On getting his first evidence that he was succeeding in this, which he had repeatedly attempted through seven years, he wrote to a friend, "I am busy just now again on electromagnetism, and I think I have got hold of a good thing, but can't say. It may be a weed instead of a fish that, after all my labour, I may at last pull up." Over the next nine days he arrived at all the major results that he sought.

Faraday was appointed in 1833 to a professorship for life in the Royal Institution. What is sometimes called his "first period of discovery" lasted until 1841, when he found that he needed rest. By that time he had carried out also the quantitative work on electrolysis described in Chapter 2. In 1845 he started his second period of research, in the course of which he discovered the phenomenon of diamagnetism — the property of being repelled by both poles of a magnet, possessed by many materials — and also the magnetic rotation of the plane of polarized light. During his last few years, finding that his memory was failing and his mental powers generally declining, this extraordinary man contentedly gave up scientific work.

found effect on these pictures of electricity. In that year William Nicholson attached brass wires to each side of a voltaic pile, dipped their free ends in a tube of river water, and noticed that the brass oxidized rapidly on one of the wires and that bubbles formed along the other. Identifying the gas in the bubbles as hydrogen, Nicholson recognized that the passage of the current was decomposing the water into its constituent elements, hydrogen and oxygen.

Many other investigators promptly examined the effects of passing an electric current through solutions of various salts in water. William Cruickshank succeeded in decomposing the chlorides of sodium and magnesium in this way, and laid the foundations for the electroplating process by using an electric current to deposit metallic silver and copper from solutions of their salts. In 1807 Sir Humphry Davy even decomposed potash and soda, which had previously been thought to be chemical elements, by moistening those solids and passing electric current through them. In thus isolating the metals sodium and potassium, Sir Humphry set the stage for the isolation of many elements that combine with others so avidly that they are difficult to separate by chemical means.

These observations still gave no quantitative picture of the relations between the electrical currents and their chemical effects. How fast would the current liberate hydrogen in Nicholson's experiment? How much current would deposit how much copper in Cruickshank's experiment? In 1830, Michael Faraday began a series of experiments designed to answer such questions as these.

Faraday's Electrochemical Experiments

Passing an electrical current through a solution of one salt or another, Faraday first examined what happened when he kept the current constant and varied other things, such as the size of the electrodes dipping into the solution. He found that, for a given current, the amount of chemical action is independent of the size of the electrodes and proportional to the time that the current flows. Summarizing his conclusions from this part of his work, Faraday wrote, "All these facts combine into, I think, an irresistible mass of evidence, proving the truth of the important proposition which I at first laid down—namely, that the chemical power of a current of electricity is in direct proportion to the absolute quantity of electricity which passes."

Faraday then went on to compare quantitatively the results that he obtained using many different salts. He found that the amount of a substance liberated by a given quantity of electricity varies from one substance to another. To each of the liberated substances that he investigated, he was able to assign a number that he called its "electrochemical equivalent." Finally he reached conclusions that he summarized in two propositions: "X. Electrochemical equivalents are always consistent, i.e., the same number which represents the equivalent of a sub-

---

JOHN DALTON (1766-1844) was born at Eaglesfield, England, to a weaver in poor circumstances who belonged to the Society of Friends. He was educated by his father and by a teacher at the local Quakers' school. The teacher retired when John was 12 years old, and the boy started teaching in his place, but the pay was so poor that after two years John turned to farming. After another year he left his village to become assistant to a cousin who kept a school at Kendal. He stayed there for twelve years, managing the school jointly with his elder brother after his cousin retired.

DALTON

Dalton was befriended by a blind philosopher, John Gough, who taught him some science and in 1793 secured a post for him at New College in Manchester to teach mathematics and natural philosophy. He occupied this position until 1799 when the college was moved to York, and then turned himself into a "public and private teacher of mathematics and chemistry." He remained in Manchester for the rest of his life, becoming in 1817 the president of the Manchester Literary and Philosophical Society.

Here surely was a man of humble origin and of original mind, quite off the beaten track. While still in Kendal he had contributed solutions of problems to the "Gentlemen's" and "Ladies' Diaries," and had begun a meteorological record that he continued for fifty-seven years, entering more than 200,000 observations. Soon after arriving in Manchester, he wrote a paper on "Extraordinary facts relating to the vision of colours," which gave the earliest account of colorblindness, since known as Daltonism. Papers followed on many diverse subjects—rain and dew and the origin of springs of water, heat, steam, the color of the sky, the reflection and refraction of light, the auxiliary verbs of the English language.

Apparently Dalton characteristically performed his experiments with rough and inaccurate instruments, even though better could readily be had. Sir Humphry Davy described him as "a very coarse experimenter," who "almost always found the results he required, trusting to his head rather than his hands."

stance, A, when it is separating from a substance, B, will also represent A when separating from a third substance, C. Thus 8 is the electrochemical equivalent of oxygen, whether separating from hydrogen, or tin, or lead; and 103.5 is the electrochemical equivalent of lead, whether separating from oxygen, or chlorine, or iodine. XI. Electrochemical equivalents coincide, and are the same, with ordinary chemical equivalents."

Today these conclusions are usually summarized in a statement known as *Faraday's Laws*: The mass of a substance liberated from an electrolyte by the passage of a current is proportional to (1) the total quantity of electricity that passes through the electrolyte and (2) the chemical equivalent weight of the substance liberated.

Dalton's Combining Weights

The "ordinary chemical equivalents," with which Faraday identified his electrochemical equivalents, had been determined by John Dalton some thirty years earlier from his measurements of the proportions in which the different elements combine with one another to form chemical compounds. Thus, to use Faraday's own example, the relative weights of oxygen and lead that combine to form the common yellow oxide of lead turn out to be oxygen 16, lead 207. Dalton's measurements had given a strong boost to the atomic hypothesis of the constitution of matter. Everyone recognized that the simplest way to explain the constant *combining weights* of the elements is to suppose that each element consists of little atoms whose actual weights stand in the same ratio as the combining weights.

Indeed, even before Faraday's work, Theodor Grotthus proposed an atomic mechanism for the electrolyses which Nicholson and Cruickshank were reporting. He suggested that, when a substance is decomposed by an electric current, its molecules behave somewhat as Figure 5 portrays. Each molecule exchanges an atom with its next neighbor, freeing an atom of each species to deposit on the two opposite electrodes.

This picture explained the central fact of electrolysis satisfactorily: Products are liberated at the electrodes while the intervening liquid stays unchanged. But the notion that only electrical currents cause the shifts that Grotthus visualized is in poor accord with some of the chemical behavior of these solutions. For example, when a solution of silver nitrate is mixed

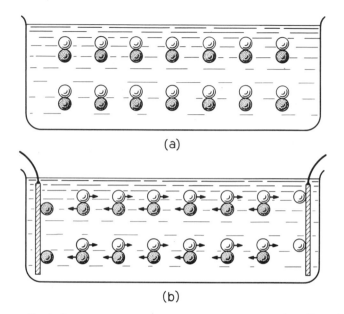

(a)

(b)

FIGURE 5 – GROTTHUS VISUALIZED ELECTROLYSIS *as a systematic switching of the allegiances of the atoms in neighboring molecules. The molecules swimming in the solution are undisturbed (a) until current passes through the solution, when the atoms begin to play the game of musical chairs, interrupted by the electrodes (b).*

with a solution of sodium chloride, the mixture promptly deposits a dense white precipitate of silver chloride. Apparently the atomic ingredients of two different molecules — the silver in silver nitrate, and the chlorine in sodium chloride — can shift over very rapidly, and under other influences than an electric current.

Conduction by Ions

To Rudolph Clausius these facts suggested that the atomic ingredients of such compounds are interchanging constantly in their solutions. In his opinion an electric current merely introduces a directive influence on these shifts, which are occurring spontaneously anyway.

But what is the source of that directive influence? Why should an electric current tend to push the two ingredients in opposite directions? In 1879 Friedrich Kohlrausch brought together several ideas, which had been growing for many years in the minds of many investigators, into a theory of electrolytic conduction that would explain that influence.

Even before Faraday's work, Sir Humphry Davy and Jöns Berzelius had suggested that the chemical combination of atoms into molecules is effected by electrical attractions, such as Coulomb had described, between electrical charges carried by the atoms. In Kohlrausch's picture those atoms, by carrying those charges, also feel attractions and repulsions from *any* electrical charges—in particular from those on the electrodes employed in the electrolysis. Thus, if sodium chloride is formed by the attraction between positive charges on sodium atoms and nega-

---

RUDOLF JULIUS EMMANUEL CLAUSIUS (1822-1888) *was one of a generation of great German and Austrian physicists— men such as Ludwig Boltzmann and Ernst Mach—who devoted themselves entirely to theoretical rather than experimental studies of their science. Born at Köslin in Pomerania, he attended the gymnasium at Stettin and the university at Berlin, and took his degree at Halle in 1848. Two years later he was appointed professor of physics in the royal artillery and engineer ing school, and privatdocent in the uni-*

CLAUSIUS

versity, at Berlin. He went to Zürich, Switzerland, five years later, accepting concurrent professorships in the university and the polytechnic. He returned to Germany in 1867 as professor of physics at Würzburg, and two years later moved into the professorship at Bonn which he held for the rest of his life. During the Franco-Prussian War he headed an ambulance corps of Bonn students—a misuse of its resources of talent by a national government that is unfortunately typical.

Clausius' major contributions to physics lie in the fields of thermodynamics and the kinetic theory of gases. To him is due a celebrated thermodynamical statement: "We can express the fundamental laws of the universe which correspond to the two fundamental laws of the mechanical theory of heat in the following simple form. (1) The energy of the universe stays constant. (2) The entropy of the universe tends toward a maximum." Clausius developed the kinetic theory to the point where he could make numerical calculations with it, such as that of the mean free path of a molecule, and also discovered a powerful mechanical theorem, the "virial theorem," which turns out to be as valid in modern wave mechanics as in the "classical" mechanics of his day. These achievements overshadow his contribution to the theory of electrolysis mentioned on page 22; but that contribution, which found little favor at the time, grew at the hands of Arrhenius and others into the theory of dissociation that we hold today.

tive charges on chlorine atoms, and if the resulting molecules of sodium chloride are continually changing their partners in solution (as Clausius suggested), then one would expect that during those exchanges the sodium atoms would be nudged a little toward the negatively charged electrode, and the chlorine atoms would be nudged in the other direction.

Two years later Hermann von Helmholtz delivered a famous "Faraday lecture" in which he pointed out an important logical consequence of these ideas: "If we accept the hypothesis that elementary substances are composed of atoms, we cannot well avoid concluding that electricity also is divided into elementary portions which behave like atoms of electricity."

Of course those atoms of electricity are unlike material atoms in one respect. Whereas elementary matter comes in about one hundred kinds, electricity comes in only two kinds—positive and negative—whose indivisible units appear to have the same size. In 1881 Johnstone Stoney christened that unit of electrical quantity the "electron."

So far the conduction of electricity through solutions of salts had been thought to depend on the momentary freedom of atoms

---

KOHLRAUSCH

FRIEDRICH WILHELM KOHLRAUSCH (1840-1910), *following the path of his father, pursued a lifelong interest in electricity and magnetism. He held professorships of physics in a succession of German universities, and finally succeeded Helmholtz as president of the Reichsanstalt at Charlottenburg.*

Kohlrausch's most important investigations dealt with the conduction of electricity through solutions of salts. He devised a method for measuring the conductivities of such solutions, using alternating current, which minimizes the disturbing effects of "polarization" by the piling-up of the charge carried by the migrating ions. With such apparatus he investigated the variation of the conductivity with the concentration of the solution, and showed that the ratio of the two approaches an upper limit for infinite dilution, where the dissolved salt is most completely dissociated into its component ions. Kohlrausch derived a theoretical relation between that ratio and the sum of the velocities of the positive and negative ions. From that sum, combined with the ratio of the velocities of the positive and negative ions determined by other investigators, Kohlrausch was able to calculate the absolute velocities of the separate ions.

in the act of exchanging their molecular partners. In 1887 Svante Arrhenius modified that picture into a form that has since remained essentially unchanged. He suggested that the molecules of a salt in solution are largely dissociated into their constituent charged atoms at all times, as Figure 6 suggests, not just during the isolated moments at which those atoms are flying from one molecule to another.

Arrhenius had powerful arguments for his view, stemming from several properties of salt solutions. One of those properties is the temperature at which a solution freezes. In this respect, most solutions of substances that are *not* salts—for example,

---

JÖNS JAKOB BERZELIUS (1779-1848) *was born near Linköping, Sweden. His studies of chemistry and medicine at Uppsala brought him the M.D. degree in 1802, and he immediately joined the faculty of botany and pharmacy at the University of Stockholm. At first he concerned himself with questions of physiological chemistry, but in 1807 he turned to his principal lifework, elucidating the compositions of chemical compounds by use of the law of multiple proportions and its atomic interpretation (pages 34-36). Continuing*

BERZELIUS

this work as professor of chemistry in the Caroline Medico-Chirurgical Institution of Stockholm, Berzelius made careful determinations of the atomic and molecular weights of some 2000 substances. The publication of his results in 1818 coincided with his ennoblement by his sovereign, Charles XIV, and his election as perpetual secretary to the Stockholm Academy of Sciences.

But even earlier he had joined with Wilhelm Hisinger in studying the electrolysis of salt solutions with the aid of the "pile" that Volta had just discovered (Figure 3). This work led him to formulate an electrochemical theory of the formation of compounds, published in 1814, in which he put forward the "dualistic hypothesis" that the atoms of the elements are electrically polarized, and positive and negative elements join together in compounds. He even extended these ideas into organic chemistry, proposing that groups of atoms can form compound "radicles," positive and negative, which then join together as elements would. Though not acceptable in so simple a form, Berzelius' idea founded the development of the radical theory of organic chemistry. He also invented the system of notation used today to formulate the composition of chemical compounds, in which a one-or-two-letter symbol is used for each elementary species, and a numerical subscript gives the number of atoms of that species taking part in a compound— for example, H_2O in the case of water.

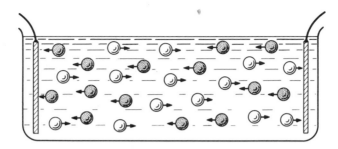

Figure 6 – TODAY'S PICTURE OF ELECTROLYSIS *is due to Arrhenius. The atoms swim independently in the solution as charge-bearing ions, which are attracted by the charges on the electrodes.*

the antifreeze in an automobile radiator—behave in an especially simple way. As more and more of such a substance is dissolved, the solution freezes at a lower and lower temperature. So long as the solution is not too concentrated, the amount of that lowering is directly proportional to the concentration of the dissolved molecules—to the number of those molecules in a unit volume of the solution. Furthermore, the lowering depends *only on the number* of dissolved molecules, and not on what the substance is. But dissolved salts lower the freezing temperature more than that: They behave as if each molecule of the salt contributed two molecules to the solution. Clearly that behavior can be explained by supposing that each molecule of the salt is permanently dissociated by the solution into the two constituents that migrate to the opposite electrodes when the solution is electrolyzed.

Thus by the beginning of this century it had been agreed that there is an ultimate unit of electricity, whose amount is the same for both positive and negative electricity. Electrical currents are carried through solutions of salts by bits of matter of atomic size, each bearing one or more of these units of electrical charge, which migrate under the electrical forces exerted on them. Faraday had given to the migrating atoms the name *ions*— the travelers—and today we apply that name to any atom or small group of atoms that bears an electrical charge.

Conduction Through Metals

But these conclusions, drawn mostly from studies of solutions, are seemingly helpless to explain the most conspicuous case of conduction of electricity—conduction through metals. Electricity can pass through metals for an indefinite time without liberating any substances at the places where it enters and leaves the metal. The conducting metal seems completely at rest; it gives no evidence that any of its atoms is drifting in the direction of the electrical current.

Investigations quite separate from those just described provided the evidence and ideas that finally led to our present understanding of electrical conduction in metals. Unexpectedly

HELMHOLTZ

HERMANN LUDWIG FERDINAND VON HELMHOLTZ (1821-1894) *was a delicate and studious child; his father, a teacher of philology and philosophy in Potsdam, directed him toward the study of nature. But his family's poverty did not permit him to follow a strictly scientific course of study, and he became a surgeon in the Prussian army. Soon, however, his papers on scientific subjects—for example, on his discovery of the nerve cells in ganglia - brought him to notice, and from the time he was 28 years old he held professorships, first of physiology and later of physics, in German universities.*

Helmholtz's work traversed an extraordinary range of scientific subjects. He investigated animal heat and animal electricity, studied the velocity of nervous impulses, and examined muscular contractions, using apparatus in which muscles recorded their own movements on a smoked glass plate. His work in physiological optics and physiological acoustics furnished many splendid examples of what can be accomplished by someone who crosses borderlines between the established branches of science. He measured the radii of curvature of the "crystalline lens" of the eye for near and far vision, explained the mechanism by which the eye focusses, and showed how the two eyeballs move in order to secure single vision. Similarly, he explained the mechanism of the bones and the cochlea within the ear.

Some of his most famous researches dealt with the physics and physiology of musical sounds. He was the first to analyze complex sounds into their component single-pitch sounds, and to verify the analysis by synthesizing the complex sounds from their ingredients. He also founded the fixed-pitch theory of vowel tones—the theory that each vowel has a recognizable pitch, independent of the note on which it is sung, which is determined by the resonance of the mouth cavity.

In later years Helmholtz turned away from these physiological investigations toward pure physics. He contributed to the development of the laws of mechanics, assisting especially in establishing the principle of the conservation of energy and the principle of "least action." His interest in electrical oscillations inspired and assisted his favorite pupil, Heinrich Hertz, to demonstrate that electromagnetic waves can be produced and propagated through space with the speed of light.

the evidence came mostly from studying the electrical properties of gases, and not from studying metals directly.

Fortunately for all of us, air at ordinary atmospheric pressure is a very good electrical insulator. Nevertheless at high voltages sparks of electricity will fly through it. As early as 1752 it occurred to William Watson, experimenting with such sparks, to see what would happen if he reduced the air pressure. He exhausted

---

ARRHENIUS

SVANTE AUGUST ARRHENIUS (1859-1927) *was born at the castle of Wijk near Uppsala, Sweden. As a child he showed unusual mathematical ability, and he entered the University of Uppsala at the age of 17 to study physics. He transferred to Stockholm, but returned to Uppsala to take his doctor's degree with a remarkable thesis, "Galvanic Conduction in Electrolytes." The second of its two parts contained the revolutionary ideas of electrolytic dissociation, referred to on page 26, that later won him the Nobel Prize in chemistry. At the time, however, they were largely ignored, and Arrhenius has told an anecdote that illustrates what often happens to radically new ideas.*

"I came to my professor, Cleve, whom I admired very much, and I said, 'I have a new theory of electrical conductivity as a cause of chemical reactions.' He said, 'This is very interesting,' and then he said, 'Good-bye.' He explained to me later that he knew very well that there are so many different theories formed, and that they are almost all certain to be wrong for after a short time they disappeared; and therefore, by using the statistical manner of forming his ideas, he concluded that my theory also would not exist long."

Arrhenius' breadth of interest and creativity continued through forty years of work at the University of Stockholm and the Nobel Institute for Physical Chemistry. He made many contributions to exact biochemistry, especially in the application of physical chemistry to explain the action of toxins and antitoxins. He was also busy with problems of cosmogony, and was one of the first to emphasize the importance of the pressure of light in cosmic phenomena, pointing out that the repulsion of the tails of comets from the sun could be explained that way. He proposed that the universe might not be "running down," as the second law of thermodynamics suggests, but that the availability of energy, degraded in bodies in the solar state, might be elevated in bodies in the nebular state. He also proposed the bold idea that life is constantly emitted from habitable worlds as spores which diffuse through the universe, and a few of which find habitation on other worlds that have reached the habitable stage.

the air as well as he could from a tube three feet long and three inches in diameter, and found that an electrical discharge passed through it much more readily. Moreover the appearance of the sparks altered: They became thicker and fainter, and looked somewhat like flame. Later Faraday also examined electrical discharges in rarefied air, and noticed that there was a glowing region around the negative electrode and a glowing column projecting from the positive electrode, separated from each other by a dark space.

After the invention in 1850 of mercury pumps for exhausting air, the better vacuums that they produce enabled investigators to pursue such studies more fruitfully. Johann Hittorf found that, as the pressure in the discharge tube is progressively reduced, the glow around the negative electrode broadens and thickens

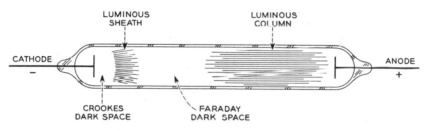

FIGURE 7 – AT LOW PRESSURE, *cathode rays proceed from the cathode through the "Crookes dark space." By reducing the pressure further, that dark space can be made to occupy a large part of the tube.*

and moves away from the electrode, leaving a dark space there also, as Figure 7 shows. When that second dark space gets broad enough to reach the walls of the glass tube that contains the discharge, the glass which meets the dark space glows green. In 1869 he reported experiments suggesting that something— he called it "light"—was proceeding outward from the cathode in straight lines. In particular he found that objects placed in the tube between the cathode and the walls would cast sharp "shadows" on the luminous glass.

Crookes and Cathode Rays

Three years later Sir William Crookes began a study of these so-called "cathode rays" that made their nature much more clear. Reducing the air pressure in the discharge tube until the dark space around the cathode expanded to fill the entire tube, he

SIR WILLIAM CROOKES (1832-1919), *a native of London, studied at the Royal College of Chemistry, and throughout his life pursued both chemical and physical studies. At the age of 19 he became assistant to August von Hofmann, the German organic chemist who had come to England to direct the new Royal College at the urging of Queen Victoria's German Prince Consort, and whose enthusiastic teaching over twenty years had great influence on chemical progress in Britain. In 1854 Crookes went to Oxford as a mete-*

CROOKES

orologist in the Radcliffe observatory, but after a year there and another as a chemist at Chester he returned to London, and thereafter he conducted research at a private laboratory that he set up at his house.

In 1861 Crookes carried out spectroscopic studies on sludges left from the commercial manufacture of sulfuric acid, and observed a bright green spectroscopic line that had not been noticed before. That observation led him to the discovery and isolation of the element thallium, whose chemical and physical properties he investigated minutely over the next eight years.

While determining the atomic weight of the newly discovered element, Crookes noticed that a sample of the metal seemed to be heavier when cold than when hot. He ascribed this effect to a "repulsion from radiation," and generalized his observation in the statement that a body in a vacuum tends to move away from a hotter body. Following this principle he designed the "Crookes radiometer" or "light-mill" which at first he believed would convert the energy of light directly into mechanical energy. From further experiments, at the hands especially of Sir Arthur Schuster, the light-mill was found to depend on thermal effects in the residual gas in the enclosure of the radiometer, and Crookes himself provided the correct theory of the device in 1876.

It was this work that led Crookes into his famous researches on the discharge of electricity through rarefied gases, described on page 29. From these researches he developed a theory of "radiant matter" or matter in a "fourth state" (the other three being solid, liquid and gas) which was the forerunner of today's picture of cathode rays as a stream of electrons.

In 1883 Crookes returned to spectroscopy, as a tool to inquire into the constitution of the "rare earths" (page 40). His work in this area was less fortunate than his earlier work on thallium, and the elucidation of this difficult problem in inorganic chemistry was accomplished by other workers. With characteristic eagerness and energy he undertook research on radium as soon as it was discovered by Marie and Pierre Curie in 1898, and he invented the spinthariscope, in which traces of radioactivity are detected by the phosphorescence that they produce on a zinc sulfide screen. He became interested also in psychic phenomena and attempted to correlate them with more familiar physical laws.

was able to perform cleaner experiments, in more space, than his predecessors. In some of these experiments he focussed the cathode rays by using a concave cathode and found that objects placed at the focal point are strongly heated.

But his most important experiment, diagrammed in Figure 8, used a narrow beam obtained by passing the cathode rays through a slit. In 1879 he found that such a beam is bent when a magnet is placed outside the tube, and showed that the direction of the deflection is that which would be taken by a wire carrying an electric current toward the cathode. Now the conventional way of describing the direction of an electrical current is to speak of the direction in which positive charges would move to carry the current. Negative charges moving in the opposite direction would carry the same current. Thus Sir William's observation confirmed a suggestion, made earlier by Cromwell Varley, that the cathode rays are a stream of negatively charged particles issuing from the cathode.

But controversy about the nature of cathode rays continued. Some scientists, placing emphasis on the facts that the rays have a straight trajectory, excite phosphorescence, and act upon photographic plates, believed that they were some form of light, perhaps of very short wave length. Others, placing emphasis on the bending of the rays by a magnetic field, believed that they were negatively charged particles moving with great velocity.

In 1894 Philipp Lenard, investigating the power of the rays to penetrate matter, made measurements that seemed to confirm the former idea. He found that the mass per unit area of a layer of matter that reduces the rays to half intensity is about the same

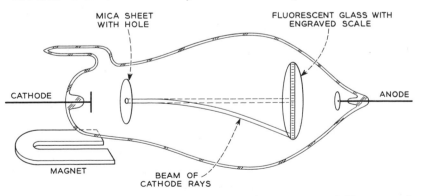

FIGURE 8 – DEFLECTION OF CATHODE RAYS *by a magnetic field convinced Crookes that they are made of negatively charged particles, not ultraviolet light.*

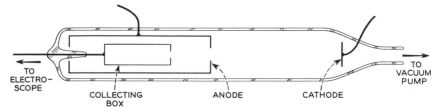

FIGURE 9 - BY DETECTING A NEGATIVE CHARGE, *on an electroscope connected to a box that collected cathode rays, Jean Perrin provided further evidence that those rays are made of negatively charged particles.*

whatever the composition of the layer—whether gold or air. Projecting the rays through a thin aluminum window in his discharge tube, he found that they could still be detected several centimeters away through the outside air. It is hard to believe that the penetrating power of a stream of charged atoms would be so large.

On the other hand, the following year Jean Perrin provided an especially direct confirmation of the idea that cathode rays are charged particles. He directed a beam of the rays through a small opening in one end of a closed metal cylinder from which a wire passed through the wall of the discharge tube to an electroscope, as Figure 9 shows. When the beam entered the cylinder, the electroscope showed a deflection that he could identify as due to negative electrification.

Thomson Identifies the Electron

Now, if the cathode rays consist of particles of matter, the matter should have mass, unlike light. In 1897 several investigators, especially Sir Joseph John Thomson, devised methods for measuring the mass of the particles presumed to compose those rays. They found that the mass must be about one two-thousandth of the mass of the lightest known atom, hydrogen. Here was a form of matter theretofore unrecognized. But it must be a constituent of many forms of matter already known: All those forms, made into cathodes in discharge tubes, would emit cathode rays. And Sir Joseph went on to show that the negative charge emitted by hot bodies into a vacuum has the same properties as the cathode rays.

If each of the particles composing cathode rays has a mass so much less than an atom, it might be expected to have also a size much smaller than an atom. Thomson pointed out that the small size of the particles would explain the extraordinary penetrating power observed by Lenard. Indeed, all subsequent research has confirmed the idea that cathode rays are made of negatively charged material particles. It was natural to assume that the charge on one of these particles is the same as the smallest charge found on an ion in electrolytic experiments — in other words, that it corresponds with the atomic unit of charge. The name *electron*, given by Stoney to that unit, was therefore adopted as the name for the newly discovered particle.

Since matter of wide variety had been shown to emit these electrons, it was natural to suppose also that the atoms composing matter are built up out of electrons in combination with enough positive electricity to make the atom electrically neutral as a whole. Then the ions found in salt solutions could be visualized as electrically neutral atoms that have become positively or negatively electrified by losing or gaining one or more electrons. Along these lines, Thomson rapidly developed a theory of the constitution of atoms which formed the foundation for today's picture of atoms, as the next chapter describes.

THOMSON

SIR JOSEPH JOHN THOMSON (1856-1940) *was born near Manchester, and educated there and at Cambridge. During his entire life, his work was centered at Cambridge University, where he became successively a fellow, a lecturer in physics, the director of the Cavendish Laboratory, and Master of Trinity College.*

Thomson's earliest work dealt with the properties of vortex rings. But he soon turned to a study of the conduction of electricity through gases. The patience and brilliance of his attack on this problem led finally to his identification of the electron and the determination of the ratio of its charge to its mass, for which he was awarded the Nobel Prize for physics in 1906.

As its director, "J. J." developed the Cavendish Laboratory into the great research institution that Ernest Rutherford inherited in 1918. No doubt a university regulation that came into force in 1895 had much to do with the rapid growth in the eminence of the laboratory. By that regulation graduates of other universities could be admitted to Cambridge as "Research Students," and that possibility attracted workers from many countries. But Thomson himself has recorded that mature students from other countries were surprised, and at first irritated, by a college restriction which obliged them to be in their rooms before a certain time at night.

3 Atoms

"The most important discoveries of the laws, methods, and progress of Nature have nearly always sprung from the examination of the smallest objects which she contains." So wrote the great Eighteenth Century naturalist, the Chevalier de Lamarck. A century after he made the remark, its truth received especially triumphant justification from the electron. During our century, the electronic theory of matter has brought a remarkable degree of order into our pictures of how matter behaves. In pursuing the story of how those pictures have arisen, it is well to heed Lamarck's advice — to examine our pictures of individual atoms and molecules before assembling them into pieces of matter large enough to be seen.

As the last chapter mentioned, the idea that matter is ultimately composed of little atomic units — an idea that arose at least two thousand years ago — gained especial impetus about 1800 from quantitative chemical experiments. John Dalton's assignment of combining weights to the chemical elements strongly suggested that chemical compounds come in little molecules, each consisting of a few closely associated atoms of the elements.

Valencies of Elements

Analysis of many such compounds soon brought out an interesting consistency in the proportions by which the elements combine. Each element appeared to have a definite "combining power." For example, one combining weight of oxygen reacts with two such weights of hydrogen to form water, and one weight of carbon combines with four weights of hydrogen to form methane. This suggests that the combining power of carbon is twice as great as that of oxygen, and the suggestion is borne out by the fact that one weight of carbon combines with two weights of oxygen to form carbon dioxide.

Accordingly chemists came to assign a number to each chemical element, called its *valency*, which measures its combining

34

power with its fellows. Thus hydrogen is given valency one and oxygen valency two because one atomic weight of oxygen will combine with two atomic weights of hydrogen. And more generally they assign to any atomic species a valency equal to the number of atomic weights of hydrogen that will combine with one atomic weight of the species.

Bonds Between Atoms

Correspondingly, the atomistic picture of water portrays that substance as a collection of water molecules, each containing two atoms of hydrogen and one of oxygen. It is tempting to diagram the molecule as in Figure 10, with a *bond* connecting

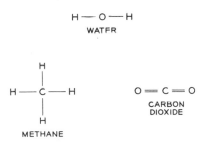

FIGURE 10 – IN CHEMISTS' DIAGRAMS *of molecules, lines are often used to signify bonds between atoms. The number of lines connected to each atom equals the valency of the atom's species and shows, for example, that hydrogen has valency one, oxygen valency two, and carbon valency four.*

each atom of hydrogen to the atom of oxygen. Then, counting the number of bonds in which each atom participates, you again assign valency one to hydrogen and valency two to oxygen.

Having assigned valency one to hydrogen, you can assign valency four to carbon, in recognition of the fact that one atomic weight of carbon combines with four atomic weights of hydrogen to form methane. To be sure, carbon and oxygen will not only form carbon dioxide but will also combine in one-to-one proportion into carbon monoxide. But carbon monoxide behaves in many ways as if it were somewhat "unsaturated," and it readily burns in oxygen to form carbon dioxide.

In order to retain the method of diagramming a molecule by bonds, making the number of bonds formed by each atom equal to the valency of its species, the carbon atom must be connected by *double bonds* with each oxygen atom in a carbon dioxide molecule. Such a diagram immediately suggests a question: Is

DMITRI IVANOVICH MENDELEYEV (1834-1907) *was born in Tobolsk, Siberia, the youngest of seventeen children. That same year his father, a school teacher, was stricken with total blindness and forced into retirement, and his mother set about supporting them all by reestablishing and managing a glassworks once owned by her family. She was indeed a remarkable woman: In a time and country where women were not schooled, she had educated herself by repeating the lessons assigned to her elder brother.*

MENDELEYEV

As her youngest son grew, she observed his interest in natural science, stimulated by contacts with some of the political exiles in Siberia, and she decided to make a scientist of him. Undaunted by her husband's death in 1847 and the destruction of her glassworks by fire, she journeyed to Moscow with her son and a daughter, to enter him in the university. In that she was unsuccessful, but after a year of effort she did succeed in placing him in the Central Pedagogic Institute in St. Petersburg, and she lived just long enough to see him graduate as a teacher.

After teaching in the Crimea and Odessa, Mendeleyev returned to St. Petersburg, took his master's degree in chemistry, and started an academic career that carried him to Paris, Heidelberg, and back to St. Petersburg to take his doctor's degree in 1861 and become professor of chemistry. He soon became eminent, both as a productive research chemist and a stimulating teacher. His 262 printed publications cover a wide range of chemical subjects, from the composition of minerals to the heats of combustion of organic compounds. He was commissioned by the Russian government to investigate the oil industry at Baku and the naphtha springs in the Caucasus, and he visited America to study the oil fields in Pennsylvania. During the latter part of his life, retired from the university, he was Director of the Bureau of Weights and Measures.*

Mendeleyev's two-volume Principles of Chemistry (1869-71), *which was long a standard Russian textbook, contains his first full statement of the Periodic Law which spread his fame throughout the scientific world. Together with Lothar Meyer, whose work on the periodicity of the elements had paralleled Mendeleyev's, he was awarded the Davy Medal of the Royal Society of London in 1882, and he received that society's Copley Medal in 1905. By the time of his death, his great generalization was acknowledged to be the most important chemical principle put forward since the atomic theory was established.*

Springing from a Russia not familiar to the Western world, Mendeleyev was its only representative to most of those who met him in Europe and America. They remembered his tall, slightly stooped figure and his deep-set bright blue eyes. They remarked upon his flowing hair, which was cut once a year, each spring. He was their "grand Russian of the province of Tver."

a double bond twice as strong as a single bond? To answer it, the energy required to break a double bond in some kind of molecules must be compared with the energy required to break a single bond between atoms of the same species in some other kind of molecules. Rather surprisingly, the comparison shows that a double bond *is* often almost twice as strong as a single bond. Hence this method of diagramming, originated merely to display the relative combining weights of atomic species, turns out to represent also some features of the strengths of the interatomic forces.

Proceeding through the list of atomic species, you can set up a consistent scheme of valencies which describes the chemical behavior of many of the species, especially those of lowest atomic weight, remarkably well. You can imagine the atoms connected by sticks, stuck into holes in the atoms, and you can imagine that the number of holes in an atom of each species is equal to its valency. Indeed, models of chemical molecules are often built in exactly that way to show how the atoms are connected together in them.

Useful as these sticks are in providing a consistent formal scheme for bringing the facts of chemistry into order, they still do not give a physical explanation of the bonds. To be sure, since a bond represented by two sticks turns out in many cases to be nearly twice as strong as a bond represented by one stick, the sticks represent the bonding better than you had any right to expect. But it was only at the beginning of this century that any deeper physical insight into chemical bonds began to emerge, as a by-product of the discovery of how atoms are built out of nuclei and electrons.

The Periodic Table

Studies of the rules of valency had already shown that the different species of atoms can be classified into groups. The species within each group have the same valency, form similar chemical compounds, and behave similarly in chemical reactions. Especially at the hands of Lothar Meyer and Dmitri Mendeleyev, the atomic species had been tabulated in a way that correlated the grouping with the atomic weights of the species.

By listing the species in order of increasing atomic weight from left to right, like ordinary reading matter, and beginning a new line when the valency begins to repeat, it turns out that the

TABLE I

BEGINNING OF MENDELEYEV'S PERIODIC TABLE

Group		I	II	III	IV	V	VI	VII	VIII
Valency		+1	+2	+3	+4 −4	(+5) −3	(+6) −2	(+7) −1	zero
Period	1	(1 H)						1 H	2 He
	2	3 Li	4 Be	5 B	6 C	7 N	8 O	9 F	10 Ne
	3	11 Na	12 Mg	13 Al	14 Si	15 P	16 S	17 Cl	18 A

Order	Name	Symbol	Weight	Order	Name	Symbol	Weight
1	Hydrogen	H	1.0	10	Neon	Ne	20.2
2	Helium	He	4.0	11	Sodium	Na	23.0
3	Lithium	Li	6.9	12	Magnesium	Mg	24.3
4	Beryllium	Be	9.0	13	Aluminum	Al	27.0
5	Boron	B	10.8	14	Silicon	Si	28.0
6	Carbon	C	12.0	15	Phosphorus	P	31.0
7	Nitrogen	N	14.0	16	Sulfur	S	32.1
8	Oxygen	O	16.0	17	Chlorine	Cl	35.5
9	Fluorine	F	19.0	18	Argon	A	39.9

elements falling under one another in the vertical columns form the groups. The procedure is especially successful for the lighter elements. The heavier elements fall into line when the tabulation is interrupted by *transition periods*, which accommodate successions of species increasing in atomic weight and having similar chemical properties.

The beginning of Mendeleyev's Periodic Table is shown in Table I. Its first three rows consist of one row of two species, followed by two rows each containing eight species. The number before the symbol for each species in the table is its *atomic number*, which is not only the number of its serial position in the table but also the number of electrons in its neutral atom. Below the table, the names and symbols of these atoms are listed

TABLE II

PERIODIC TABLE WITH TRANSITION SERIES OMITTED

Group		I	II	III	IV	V	VI	VII	VIII
Valency		+1	+2	+3	+4 −4	(+5) −3	(+6) −2	(+7) −1	zero
Period	1	(1 H)						1 H	2 He
	2	3 Li	4 Be	5 B	6 C	7 N	8 O	9 F	10 Ne
	3	11 Na	12 Mg	13 Al	14 Si	15 P	16 S	17 Cl	18 A
	4	19 K	20 Ca	31 Ga	32 Ge	33 As	34 Se	35 Br	36 Kr
	5	37 Rb	38 Sr	49 In	50 Sn	51 Sb	52 Te	53 I	54 Xe
	6	55 Cs	56 Ba	81 Tl	82 Pb	83 Bi	84 Po	85 At	86 Rn

along with their *atomic weights*, to show that the order in the table is the same as the order of increasing atomic weight.

At the table's left are the species of valency one, and at its extreme right are the *rare gases*, such as neon, of valency zero. The species on the left tend to combine with those on the right to form *salts*. The positive or negative sign attached to each valency in the table refers to the electrically positive or negative character of the ions formed by the atoms with that valency. But atoms of any species will usually form bonds of some sort with atoms of any other or even their own species.

In studying how the tabulation of Table I is continued, it is helpful to look first at an abbreviated table, Table II, which omits the transition series. The chemical similarity of the species in any one group continues to be conspicuous. The *alkali metals* in Group I all form strongly basic hydroxides closely resembling sodium hydroxide, the substance popularly called lye. The species in Group VII are called *halogens* because they will combine with the alkali metals to form salts resembling halite, the mineralogist's name for common salt (NaCl).

The principal transition series interrupt this abbreviated table between Groups II and III in its fourth, fifth, and sixth periods. Chemists often assign the species in these transition series to the eight major groups in the way shown in Table III. The assignments recognize that these species frequently show *principal valencies* appropriate to these groups. Thus copper (Cu), silver (Ag), and gold (Au) often show valency one.

But copper more often shows valency two, silver can also show that valency, and gold even shows valency three. Indeed such ambivalence characterizes most of the transition species. The "currency metals"—copper, silver, and gold—resemble one another more than they resemble the alkali metals, and in recognition of such relationships each major group in the Periodic

TABLE III
TRANSITION SERIES NOT SHOWN IN TABLE II

Group		I	II	III	IV	V	VI	VII	VIII		
Period	4	29 Cu	30 Zn	21 Sc	22 Ti	23 V	24 Cr	25 Mn	26 Fe	27 Co	28 Ni
	5	47 Ag	48 Cd	39 Y	40 Zr	41 Nb	42 Mo	43 Ma	44 Ru	45 Rh	46 Pd
	6	79 Au	80 Hg	57 La	72 Hf	73 Ta	74 W	75 Re	76 Os	77 Ir	78 Pt

TABLE IV
MORE COMPLETE TABLE
(ONLY RARE EARTHS OMITTED)

Group		I	II	III	IV	V	VI	VII	VIII
Valency		+1	+2	+3	+4 −4	(+5) −3	(+6) −2	(+7) −1	zero
Period	1	(1 H)						1 H	2 He
	2	3 Li	4 Be	5 B	6 C	7 N	8 O	9 F	10 Ne
	3	11 Na	12 Mg	13 Al	14 Si	15 P	16 S	17 Cl	18 A
	4	19 K	20 Ca	21 Sc	22 Ti	23 V	24 Cr	25 Mn	26 Fe 27 Co 28 Ni
		29 Cu	30 Zn	31 Ga	32 Ge	33 As	34 Se	35 Br	36 Kr
	5	37 Rb	38 Sr	39 Y	40 Zr	41 Nb	42 Mo	43 Ma	44 Ru 45 Rh 46 Pd
		47 Ag	48 Cd	49 In	50 Sn	51 Sb	52 Te	53 I	54 Xe
	6	55 Cs	56 Ba	57 La	72 Hf	73 Ta	74 W	75 Re	76 Os 77 Ir 78 Pt
		79 Au	80 Hg	81 Tl	82 Pb	83 Bi	84 Po	85 At	86 Rn

Table is usually divided into two subgroups, which are shown on separate lines in Table IV.

The assignment of the three similar species, iron, cobalt, and nickel, to Group VIII is a final admission of failure to force Nature into so simple a mold, for these metals bear no chemical resemblance whatever to the rare gases. Finally, the last of the principal transition periods is itself interrupted by the fourteen *rare earth* species, whose chemical resemblance to one another is so close that any one of them can be separated from the others only with difficulty.

Thomson's Idea of Atoms and Electrons

These were the facts facing J. J. Thomson at the turn of the century, when he discovered that many kinds of matter would emit cathode rays, and guessed that their atoms contain electrons. From these beginnings, he built up a theory in which atoms are constructed of negatively charged electrons and an electrically compensating body of positive charge. His theory had to leave unclear just how that positive charge is embodied. But he supposed that the charge somehow enables the electrons to traverse orbits, or to vibrate about positions of equilibrium, within the atom.

Several of Thomson's ideas anticipated those that have been placed on a firmer basis since his time. For example, he suggested that the number of electrons in the various species of atoms increases with the atomic weight of the species. He proposed that the electrons are arranged in groups or layers in an atom, and that the number of electrons in the outermost layer largely determines the chemical properties of the species. According to Thomson, the rare gas atoms must contain especially stable arrangements of electrons. An atom with one electron less than a rare gas atom — for example, chlorine — tends to acquire an extra electron and so form a negative ion. An atom with one more electron — for example, sodium — readily loses it, to form a positive ion. Atoms that readily lose electrons combine chemically with atoms that tend to acquire electrons.

These ideas of Thomson's were helpful in explaining the formation of such chemical compounds as sodium chloride, in which the two combining atomic species acquire opposite electric charges. But they did not seem to shed any light on the reasons for the many chemical combinations in which no atoms appear to become electrically charged. Hydrogen gas, for example, is made of molecules each of which contains two hydrogen atoms tightly joined. There is no reason to expect that one would acquire a positive charge, the other a negative charge, and no evidence that they do.

Nevertheless, the idea gained ground that the electrons are found in successive *shells* within the atom. Each step forward in the Periodic Table was taken to correspond with the addition of one more electron and one more compensating positive charge. In a rare-gas atom a shell of electrons is filled to capacity, and the next step puts an electron in a shell outside of those previously filled. Thus the ideas about chemical combination that Thomson had put forward could be interpreted as a striving of atoms to attain filled shells of electrons.

Figure 11 portrays the successive steps of shell-filling in the first three periods of the Periodic Table. A hydrogen atom has only one electron. A helium atom has two electrons, which complete the quota of the innermost shell. The additional electron in a lithium atom is forced to occupy the next shell. The maximum quota of that shell is completed in neon, and therefore in sodium occupancy of still another shell begins.

The Chemical Bond

In 1916 Gilbert Lewis noticed a way in which this picture of shell-filling could be extended to explain the formation of compounds in which the atoms do not acquire electric charges. He

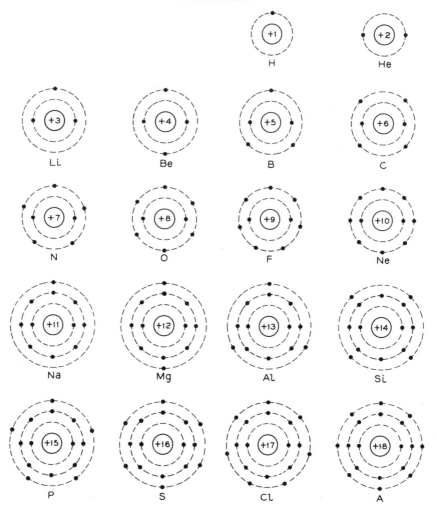

FIGURE 11 – SHELL-FILLING *in the first three periods of the Periodic Table. In each successively heavier species of atom, one electron is added and one additional positive charge is added also, along with the increased mass.*

assumed that two atoms, both with outer shells only partly filled, could also fill those shells by *sharing* electrons with each other. For example, by sharing its one electron with its partner, each of the two hydrogen atoms in a hydrogen molecule provides its only occupied shell with two electrons instead of one and thus that shell is filled like the corresponding shell of the rare gas, helium.

At first this may seem like pulling rabbits out of a hat. If each of the two atoms in a hydrogen molecule has two electrons in a shell, there may seem to be four electrons growing where only two grew before. But of course there are still really only two electrons. The shells are shells of *possibilities*, not shells of electrons. Each hydrogen atom offers two possibilities in its innermost shell, and there are two electrons available. Either electron can hop out of one of the atoms, spend a little time in the other atom, and then hop back. This is the sense in which the shell is filled by the native electron and the visiting electron.

While these formulations of chemical behavior were developing, more definite outlines were also being drawn for the physical picture of atoms. At the beginning of the century, Sir Ernest Rutherford had investigated the nature of the radiations given off from radioactive materials, in particular from uranium. He distinguished two types of radiation as *alpha rays* and *beta rays*. The latter were shown by other investigators to resemble the cathode rays discussed in Chapter 2 — to be, in fact, a high-speed stream of electrons. Sir Ernest showed that alpha rays were composed of a stream of positively charged particles, which he identified as helium atoms that have lost their electrons.

Rutherford recognized that such a stream of positively charged particles might form a valuable tool for investigating how the positive charge is embodied in atoms. He directed a narrow beam of alpha rays through a thin metal sheet, and found that a few are deviated or "scattered" by the metal through large angles. He examined mathematically what the positively charged particles would be expected to do if they were presented with various supposed arrangements of the positive charge in the atoms of the metal, and concluded that the positive charge could not be distributed uniformly through the atom, as Thomson had suggested. Indeed, the results could be explained quite exactly by supposing that the scattered particles had been caused to deviate by passing close to tiny positively charged particles within the atom.

The Planetary Atom

Thus the nuclear picture of the atom was born — a picture in which the positive charge is concentrated in a nucleus which is very small in comparison to the whole atom, and which possesses almost all the atom's mass. About that nucleus the electrons circulate much as the planets circulate about the sun.

Instead of the gravitational force that holds the solar system together, the electrical attraction between the positively charged nucleus and the negatively charged electrons holds an atom together.

RUTHERFORD

SIR ERNEST RUTHERFORD (1871-1937) *was a New Zealander who did his undergraduate study at Canterbury College in Christchurch. In 1895 he received a scholarship enabling him to go to England to work in the Cavendish Laboratory in Cambridge under J. J. Thomson. Three years later he was offered a professorship at McGill University in Canada, no doubt largely in consequence of a testimonial from Thomson: "I have never had a student with more enthusiasm or ability for original research than Mr. Rutherford and I am sure that if elected he would establish a distinguished school of Physics at Montreal."*

The nine years of Rutherford's researches at McGill attest how well Thomson knew his man. In collaboration especially with Frederick Soddy, who came to McGill from Oxford two years later, Rutherford investigated the radioactive elements uranium, thorium, and radium, announcing ultimately that "radioactivity is shown to be accompanied by electrical changes in which new types of matter are being continually produced." He described the "gamma" and "alpha" radiations emitted in this activity, and reached strong convictions, which he later confirmed, that the former were akin to X rays and that the latter were charged helium atoms. For this work he was awarded the Nobel Prize for chemistry the year after he returned to England.

From 1907 to 1919 Rutherford was professor of physics at Manchester University. Here it was that he and his students (in particular Hans Geiger and Ernest Marsden) did the work on the scattering of alpha particles which implied that each atom must be built of a tiny nucleus surrounded by a cloud of electrons. At that time Rutherford did not realize how epoch-making the work would turn out to be, especially as a result of Niels Bohr's prompt application of Max Planck's quantum theory to Rutherford's nuclear model of the atom. Much later he wrote to Geiger, "They were happy days in Manchester and we wrought better than we knew."

As head of the Cavendish Laboratory in Cambridge, from 1919 until his death, Rutherford presided over the most illustrious period of that illustrious institution. All have agreed that his energy, stimulation and direct interest were important determinants of the preeminent work that came from Cambridge. Niels Bohr has said that to those in Rutherford's laboratory it was often as if the sun suddenly began to shine when he arrived in the morning.

This planetary picture of atoms, proposed by Rutherford, was elaborated over the next fifteen years to accommodate a great variety of atomic phenomena. The orbits were said to have similar shapes to those which the planets take, or to those which they *could* take, because an inverse-square law of force applies alike to both the gravitational and electrical forces. In developing this picture, the only differences (aside from the great difference in size) might be that the planets attract one another, whereas the electrons repel one another. Thus the planets perturb one another's orbits about the sun by pulling on one another with gravitational attractions, and the electrons perturb one another's orbits about the nucleus by pushing on one another with electrical repulsions.

In fact, however, there is another difference, much more important, between an atom and the solar system. The shapes and sizes of the orbits that electrons can traverse in an atom are much more strictly limited than are the orbital shapes permitted to a planet. This limitation to move only in these permitted orbits, is a *quantum restriction*. It is not understandable in terms of the mechanical behavior familiar in visible objects; it becomes conspicuous only in the behavior of objects as small as atoms.

Planck's Quantum Theory

The quantum theory, which offers rules to describe this odd behavior was invented in 1900 by Max Planck. He was studying the results of experiments on the light radiated from a hole in an empty black cavity that had been heated until it glowed. Presumably that light is given off by the atoms at the walls of the cavity: Their heat vibrations rapidly oscillate the electric charges associated with them, and cause them to radiate the electromagnetic waves called light, much as a radio antenna radiates similar waves with longer wavelengths.

Examining the different amounts of energy radiated at different wavelengths by such a "black body," Planck was forced to conclude that the vibrating atoms do not emit or absorb light continuously but only in little packages. Each package has a definite size, in terms of its content of energy, which is directly proportional to the frequency of the light. In other words, the energy in each package is given by $E = h\nu$, where ν is the frequency and h is the constant of proportionality now called Planck's constant.

Five years later Albert Einstein made several applications of these new ideas to other puzzling phenomena—for example, the photoelectric effect, in which certain substances emit electrons when they are irradiated with light of suitable frequencies. In discussing such effects, he suggested that each package of radiant energy, $h\nu$, does not spread out from its source in all directions but is sent out in a single direction, like a particle. It has become customary to speak of such a "particle" as a *photon*.

Einstein's success in explaining these matters gave the quan-

PLANCK

MAX PLANCK (1858-1947) *was born in Kiel, Germany, the son of a professor of constitutional law. He studied in Munich and Berlin, and went on to teach physics in the universities of both cities, as well as his birthplace, becoming finally president of the Kaiser Wilhelm Society for the Advancement of Science, the highest academic post in Germany. From the outset Planck took especial interest in thermodynamics, and it was his patient and brilliant pursuit of a thermodynamical problem over twenty years that finally led him to invent the quantum theory in 1900.*

The problem is that of the equilibrium between matter and radiation: How and why do the intensities of the rays of different frequency, emitted by a hot body, change with rising temperature? To explain the measured curves of intensity against frequency, and the shift of those curves with changing temperature, Planck finally found it necessary to assume that radiation can be emitted only in tiny packets, each with energy $h\nu$, where ν is the frequency of the radiation and h is a constant now called "Planck's Constant." He announced this conclusion in 1900; by 1918 its revolutionary importance was so fully recognized that Planck received the Nobel Prize for physics.

The change which Planck's idea introduced into physical understanding cannot be overestimated. In 1925 the famous Dutch theoretical physicist H. A. Lorentz wrote, "We have now advanced so far that this constant not only furnishes the basis for explaining the intensity of radiation and the wavelength for which it represents a maximum, but also for interpreting the quantitative relations existing in several other cases among the many physical quantities it determines. I shall mention only a few: namely, the specific heat of solids, the photochemical effects of light, the orbits of electrons in the atom, the wavelengths of the lines of the spectrum, the frequency of the Roentgen rays which are produced by the impact of electrons of given velocity, the velocity with which gas molecules can rotate, and also the distances between the particles which make up a crystal."

EINSTEIN

ALBERT EINSTEIN (1879-1955), *surely one of the towering figures in the entire history of science, was a somewhat "slow starter." Born at Ulm in Germany, he spent his boyhood in Munich where his father owned electrotechnical works. When he was 15 years old, his family moved to Italy and he entered a Swiss cantonal school at Aarau. A year later his application for admission to the Polytechnic Institute in Zürich was denied because of inadequate attainment in languages and biology, but having repaired those deficiencies by home study, he was admitted the following year. He attended lectures while supporting himself by teaching mathematics and physics until his graduation in 1900. After a year as a tutor at Schaffhausen he was appointed a patent examiner in the Swiss patent office at Bern, and in this capacity over the following nine years he found time to take his Ph.D. degree and to develop and publish some of his most important ideas.*

In 1905, for example, he published his first paper on the theory of relativity, and also the first of his several papers on his light-quantum hypothesis, mentioned on page 46, which led to his law of the photoelectric effect. Two years later he published a theory of the heat capacities of solids, which employed Planck's quantum theory to explain the fact that heat capacities are smaller at low temperatures—one of the earliest achievements of quantum theory.

The importance of these papers was so conspicuous that in 1909 Einstein was appointed extraordinary professor of theoretical physics at the University of Zürich. Two years later he accepted a chair in physics at Prague, but after a year he returned to Zürich, this time as full professor at the Polytechnic. By 1913 his preeminence was so clear that a special position, Director of the Kaiser-Wilhelm Physical Institute, was created for him in Berlin, in which capacity he was permitted to spend his entire time in research, without routine duties or restrictions.

Einstein's early work in the theory of relativity had been concerned with the analysis of physical systems moving with uniform relative velocities—the "special theory" of relativity. In 1915 he expanded the analysis to include systems which are also accelerated relative to one another—the "general theory" of relativity. In 1929 he published two short papers on a "unified field theory," attempting to frame the laws of gravitation and electromagnetism in a common structure. This effort was not wholly successful; Einstein spent the rest of his life attempting to perfect such a structure, and the problem continues to occupy the attention of many other theorists.

When the Nazis began their systematic persecution of the Jews in Germany, Einstein came to the United States, accepting a permanent position with the Institute for Advanced Study in Princeton.

tum theory further stature. Bizarre though the theory seemed, it yielded answers that checked the results of experiments which no theory had been able to explain before. But its application to the structure of atoms had to await the picture of the nuclear atom that Rutherford produced in 1911.

That picture—of electrons traversing orbits about a nucleus— solved the problem of how the positive charge in an atom is embodied, but it presented new puzzles, equally formidable. If an electron is a charged particle traversing an orbit, then it should radiate electromagnetic waves. Since those waves would carry energy away from the atom, the electron should lose energy, and its orbit should change, allowing it to come constantly closer to the nucleus. As its orbit changes, the frequency with which it traverses the orbit would also change, and thus the frequency of the wave that it radiates should change. Finally, the electron should lose enough energy to fall into the nucleus; the atom should collapse to a size not much bigger than its nucleus.

Now of course atoms seem to be quite stable and uncollapsible, and the frequencies of their radiations are not continually varying. Those frequencies are very sharply defined, and characteristic of each atomic species—so characteristic that breaking up the radiation into its component colors in a spectroscope is used analytically for identifying atomic species.

Bohr's Two Postulates

In 1913 Niels Bohr successfully resolved these puzzles by extending Planck's quantum theory to the simplest atom, hydrogen. He formulated two postulates that remain valid today, despite the radical revision of the quantum theory that began in 1925. Bohr's first postulate asserted that an atomic system can exist in certain "stationary states" without radiating its energy. Each state corresponds to a definite value of the energy W of the system. If the system goes from one stationary state to another, there is a gain or loss of energy, whose amount is equal to the difference between the energies of the two states. This energy difference may be emitted or absorbed as radiation, or it may be transmitted to or from some other atomic system.

Bohr's second postulate concerned the frequency of the radiation emitted or absorbed by a system when it makes a transition between two states. If the energies of the two states are W_1 and

W_2, the frequency of the radiation is given by $h\nu = W_2 - W_1$. This postulate immediately suggests a way to picture an atom, or at least an atom containing only one electron.

First, measure in a spectrometer the frequencies of all the radiations that the atom emits. Second, using Bohr's rule, convert the frequencies to energy differences. Third, find what energies W form a consistent set that yield these differences. Fourth, calculate what possible orbits would give an electron these energies. Having done this, you can assume that, when the atom has not been excited by impact or great heat or incoming radiation, the electron will be traversing the orbit with the lowest energy—in other words, the atom will be in its *ground state*. The other orbits describe the other possible stationary states of the atom.

Figure 12 displays some results of the third step in this procedure—the *energy levels* whose differences furnish the spectral frequencies observed for hydrogen. In moving on to the fourth step, it turns out that an electron with any one of these

---

Niels Henrik David Bohr (1885-1962) *was born in Copenhagen, Denmark, the son of a professor of physiology at the university. He studied there until he took his doctor's degree in 1911, and then went to Cambridge, England, to work under Sir J.J. Thomson. The following year he moved to Manchester, where Sir Ernest Rutherford had just provided the experimental evidence for the idea that an atom is made of a small positively charged nucleus, surrounded by negatively charged electrons describing "planetary" orbits. Re-*

BOHR

turning after a year to Copenhagen, he applied Planck's quantum theory to Sir Ernest's model of the atom, to provide the very convincing quantitative results described on pages 48-50, for which he was later awarded the Nobel Prize for physics.

In 1916 Bohr became professor of theoretical physics at Copenhagen, and four years later he was appointed the first head of an institute for theoretical physics, newly formed at the university, which under his direction became one of the great intellectual centers of Europe. Bohr's theoretical insight, especially into ways of codifying experimental experience and philosophical suggestions at the same time into principles of great power and generality, have played a large part in producing our present pictures of atomic and subatomic phenomena.

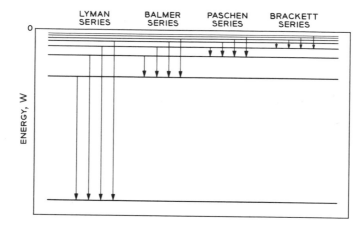

FIGURE 12 – SOME LEVELS OF ENERGY *in the hydrogen atom, worked out from the observed spectral frequencies by using Bohr's frequency postulate,* $h\nu = W_2 - W_1$. *The various series of spectral frequencies are named after the spectroscopists who examined them. The Lyman series lies in the ultraviolet frequency range. Some frequencies of the Balmer series lie in the visible range. The Paschen and Brackett series lie in the infrared range.*

energies could have many different orbits. The energy alone does not determine the orbit uniquely.

The only way to decide which is the actual orbit of the electron is to turn to other experiments — to look at how the spectral frequencies are changed by applying electric and magnetic fields to the atoms, for example. As Planck once put the matter, "Facts always form a central point about which the most important theories hinge." It is hard work to make a good physical theory — a theory that retains as much as possible of the theoretical progress of the past, and introduces a minimum of the novelty required to explain novel experimental results. Suitable rules for making choices among the possible orbits were finally worked out by Arnold Sommerfeld in 1916. Some typical orbits are shown in Figure 13.

Wave Theories

But when these methods were applied to atomic systems only slightly more complicated than the hydrogen atom, they were unsatisfactory. They could not be made to yield the energy levels spectroscopically determined in helium, the atom with two electrons instead of just one. Nor did they give correct

answers for the "hydrogen molecule-ion" — the hydrogen molecule from which one electron has been removed and the one
remaining electron circulates about two nuclei.

During the following decade, dissatisfaction with such dis-
crepancies slowly boiled up into revolution. In 1924 Louis de
Broglie suggested that a train of *waves* might be essentially
associated with any moving particle. This idea recalls Einstein's
earlier suggestion that light, previously thought of as waves,
behaves in some respects like a stream of particles, the photons.
Taken together, the two suggestions imply a curious symmetry
in Nature, by which both wave-like and particle-like behavior
can be discerned in all of Nature's fundamental processes.

Three years later, Clinton Davisson and Lester Germer confirmed de Broglie's idea by experiments in which electrons were
diffracted by a crystal of nickel; all agreed that diffraction is a
phenomenon to be expected of waves, and not of "particles"
as they had previously been understood. And by 1926, even
without waiting for such confirmation of de Broglie's idea,
Erwin Schroedinger had rushed ahead to develop a *wave mechanics* which treats all particles as if they were waves. He
used this to explain the spectroscopic data obtained from hydrogen, saying "The new conception can be generalized, and I
believe that it penetrates deeply into the true nature of the quantum rules."

Since then, wave mechanics has gone on from one triumph to
another, explaining successfully such matters as the bonding of

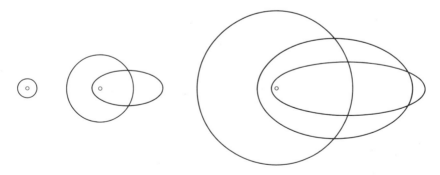

FIGURE 13 – SOME ELECTRONIC ORBITS *in hydrogen, calculated by using
Sommerfeld's rules. The smallest circular orbit, at the left, describes the stationary state whose energy falls at the lowest line in Figure 12. The other circular and elliptical orbits (to the same scale) correspond with higher energies.*

atoms in molecules and solids and the behavior of electrons in them. This newer mechanics pictures an atom as a positive nucleus surrounded by a continuous distribution of negative electricity, contributed by all the electrons, which oscillates with definite frequencies.

A vague, cloudy picture? Fortunately he who finds too great discomfort in it can resort to a somewhat more concrete interpretation of the meaning of these waves, proposed in 1926 by Max Born, in which each electron remains a distinct particle. In that picture the distribution of negative electricity is painted by the electronic particles moving rapidly in their paths. To be sure, the paths cannot be determined — only the smear that they paint. But the density of the smear at any point is a measure of the fraction of its life that an electron spends at that point. And it often turns out that an electron spends most of its time at the points which together form the orbit that the older quantum theory would have predicted.

Said Max Planck in 1926, "Surely much more will be thought and written about these questions, for theorists are numerous and paper is patient."

4 Molecules and Solids

It is sometimes said, "An electron will tell you that it is a particle any time you step up and ask it." That's not quite true: The Davisson-Germer experiment and the success of wave mechanics both tell us that it is really a wave — that an electron moving freely in space is a tiny packet of traveling waves, and that an electron in a stationary state in an atom is a standing wave, like the wave of a vibrating violin string. But Max Born's interpretation of wave mechanics, described in Chapter 3, gives us justification for clinging to the idea that an electron is a particle bearing a negative electric charge. In most of what follows, we will continue to speak of the electron as if it were a particle, invoking wave mechanics when we must in order to learn where that particle is most likely to be.

Now, using Sir Ernest Rutherford's picture of an atom, imagine what might happen when two atoms approach each other. In each atom, electrons are circulating about a central nucleus; the attraction by the positive charge of that nucleus for the negative charges of those electrons keeps the electrons from straying away. But when two atoms get close to each other, the electrons on each also feel attracted by the nucleus of the other. The electrons start to divide their allegiance between the two nuclei.

You can see in Figure 14(a) the result of that sharing. When an electron from the atom at the right strays to the atom at the left, it leaves a net positive charge on the atom that it has deserted and puts a net negative charge on the atom that it visits. Then, during that visit, the two atoms attract each other because they are oppositely charged. Of course the same thing happens if an electron from the atom on the left behaves similarly [Figure 14(b)]: The charges on the atoms are reversed, but they still attract each other.

If the electrons do not completely desert their parent atoms but wander uncertainly between them, attracted equally by both nuclei, then both atoms are left with some net positive charge,

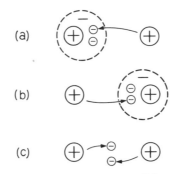

FIGURE 14 – THREE FORMAL ARRANGEMENTS *of the two electrons in a hydrogen molecule. When both electrons are near one or the other nucleus (a) and (b), the two atoms attract each other as two ions would. When the electrons are between the nuclei (c), they attract both nuclei toward them, and thus toward each other.*

as shown in Figure 14(c). Between them are the electrons, and both atoms are attracted toward that concentration of negative charge. Thus in all these cases the result is an attractive force that holds the two atoms together into a molecule.

Wave Mechanics and Bonding

It is comforting to find that wave mechanics presents essentially the same picture of the bonding between two atoms. In 1927 Walter Heitler and Fritz London calculated approximately the distribution of negative charge that wave mechanics predicts

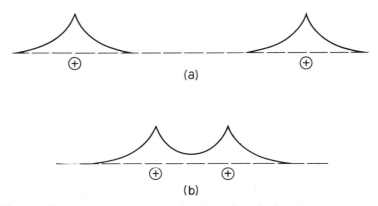

FIGURE 15 – PLOTS OF CHARGE DENSITY *can be calculated by wave mechanics, to show the distribution of negative charge about two hydrogen nuclei when the atoms are far apart (a) and when they are associated in a hydrogen molecule (b). In the latter case some negative charge, shifted into the space between the two nuclei, pulls them toward each other.*

for a hydrogen molecule. When the two component hydrogen atoms are still far apart, the charge is distributed as shown at the top of Figure 15. When the atoms get close together, the charge-clouds readjust their densities, as shown at the bottom of that figure. More charge resides between the two hydrogen nuclei, and the nuclei are attracted toward that greater concentration. But of course, as the nuclei get nearer to each other, the repulsion between their positive charges increases. Finally, the nuclei stand apart at a distance such that the repulsion between them just balances the attraction of the negative cloud for them.

This example shows the physical source of the bonding between the atoms in many sorts of molecules. When Lewis' rules, described in the last chapter, permit two atoms to share a pair of electrons, the negative charge-clouds constructed by those electrons change their shapes to provide an attractive force for the positively charged nuclei, which pulls those nuclei toward each other. Bonds of this sort are often called *covalent bonds* or *valency bonds*, to distinguish them from the attractions between two oppositely charged ions.

Ionically Bonded Solids

Ionic bonds or covalent bonds are often extended from atom to atom, until the bonded atoms are so numerous that the assembly is large enough to be seen as a piece of solid matter. A crystal of sodium chloride is a good example of a solid that is ionically bonded. It is made of equal numbers of positive sodium ions and negative chlorine ions; each sodium atom has transferred one electron to a chlorine atom. In the solid each ion takes a position in which it gets as close to the oppositely charged ions and as far from the similarly charged ions as it can.

The resulting atomic arrangement is shown in Figure 16. Each ion is immediately surrounded by six of its opposites. Notice that the crystal is not built of molecules of sodium chloride but of sodium ions and chlorine ions. There is no evidence in the atomic arrangement that these ions are paired to form molecules.

For contrast with sodium chloride, consider a crystal of diamond. It is made of carbon atoms, all identical; and like the hydrogen atoms in a molecule of hydrogen gas, they have no excuse to acquire alternate electric charges and become ions. The crystalline arrangement of the atoms in a diamond is shown

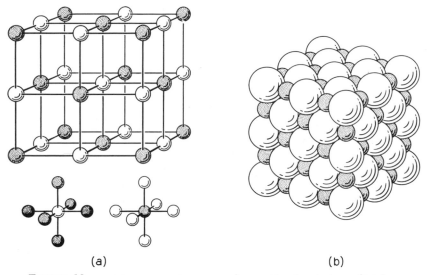

(a)   (b)

FIGURE 16 – IN SODIUM CHLORIDE, *each negative ion is immediately sur-rounded by six positive ions, and each positive ion by six negative ions, as shown at the left. Diagrams of atomic arrangements in crystals usually show just the locations of the centers of the atoms, so that the arrangements can be seen more readily. The diagram at the right shows more truly how the ions pack together. It was drawn by William Barlow, who suggested more than seventy years ago that the atoms in sodium chloride might take this arrangement. Objections were raised then that the structure does not portray the atoms as associated in diatomic molecules. But studies of sodium chloride crystals by X-ray diffrac-tion have since shown that Barlow was right: The molecules, not the structure, had to be discarded. His diagram also shows correctly that the chlorine ions are larger than the sodium ions.*

in Figure 17: Each is surrounded by four immediate neighbors at the four corners of a regular tetrahedron. Clearly each is shar-ing one of the four electrons in its outermost occupied shell of orbits with one of those neighbors, and thus it establishes a covalent bond with that neighbor.

One-Electron Bonds

Notice in both the hydrogen molecule and the crystal of dia-mond that each covalent bond is formed by a pair of electrons, of which one is donated by each of the bonded atoms. But do not conclude that bonding depends on a *pair* of electrons. A single electron will do the trick.

A molecule bonded by a single electron was mentioned in the last chapter: the *hydrogen molecule-ion*. When one electron is

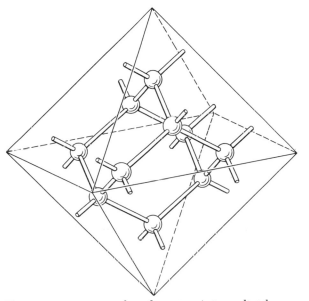

FIGURE 17 – IN A DIAMOND, *each carbon atom is immediately surrounded by four others, held to it by strong covalent bonds directed toward the four corners of a regular tetrahedron. The resulting network of bonds makes a diamond crystal a single giant molecule, and the bonds' strength gives to a diamond its extreme hardness.*

removed from a hydrogen molecule, there is only one electron left. It wanders around both hydrogen nuclei, perhaps somewhat as Figure 18 suggests; wave mechanics tells us that we cannot learn its complicated path. But we can plot, as in Figure 19, the relative lengths of time that it spends in different places, and find that it is bonding the molecule-ion by spending more time between the nuclei than elsewhere.

Experiment shows that the energy required to break this bond

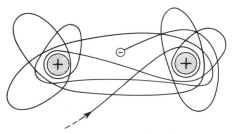

FIGURE 18 – AN ELECTRON BONDING *a molecule traverses a complicated orbit, so rapidly that the much heavier nuclei can respond only to its time-average force. If the electron spends more time between the nuclei than elsewhere, its time-average force on the nuclei will attract them toward each other.*

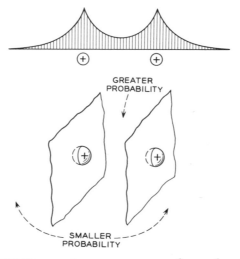

GREATER
PROBABILITY

SMALLER
PROBABILITY

FIGURE 19 – THE WAVE-MECHANICAL PICTURE *of a covalent bond formed by one electron, corresponding to the particle-picture of Figure 18.*

— to separate the two atoms — is about half that required to break the bond in an ordinary hydrogen molecule having two electrons. The prevalence of electron-pair bonds has often been rashly interpreted as betokening a mysterious force which comes into being with the pairing of electrons. But the hydrogen molecule-ion dispels that mystery by showing that a bond approximately half as strong as an electron-pair bond arises from half as many electrons. The reason that electron-pair bonds are commoner is simply that there are usually enough electrons about to form them whenever atoms offer suitable unoccupied orbits.

Bonding in Metals

The hydrogen molecule-ion is a comforting creature in still another respect. It provides preparation for understanding how the atoms are bonded in solid metals. In the hydrogen molecule-ion, each of two atoms provides two orbital possibilities in its bonding shell. If the atoms shared two electrons the orbital possibilities would be completely utilized, but there is only one electron available. The solid metals carry still further the excess in the number of orbital possibilities over the number of electrons to fill them.

Sodium, for example, forms metallic crystals with the "body-centered cubic" structure shown in Figure 20. Each sodium atom has eight others as immediate neighbors. Since the outermost occupied shell of a sodium atom contains only one electron, the arrays of neighbors offer many more possible orbits than electrons to fill them. The atoms provide a happy hunting ground of orbits for the electrons, and the electrons can stray from one atom to another, always finding a welcoming home. For this reason chemists often speak of the bonds in the hydrogen molecule-ion and the metals as *electron-deficient bonds.*

A little arithmetic may help to make definite the idea of the electron-deficient bond. First suppose that each atom attempts to make an electron-pair bond with each of its immediate neighbors. Then count the number of bonds per atom that the struc-

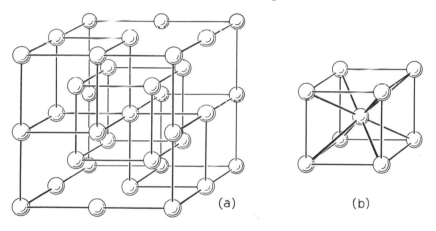

(a)   (b)

FIGURE 20 – IN THE BODY-CENTERED CUBIC *structure (a), adopted by many metals including iron and sodium, each atom has eight immediate neighbors (b), and the bonding is "electron-deficient."*

ture must have. Finally count the number of electrons per bond that are available. If that number is less than two, then the electron deficiency in the bonding is two minus that number, and that number itself is the *electron occupancy* in the bonding.

For instance, in diamond each carbon atom has four neighbors. Each bond involves a pair of neighbors, and therefore there are two bonds per atom. Each atom has four electrons in its outermost occupied shell. Since there are four available electrons per atom and two bonds per atom, there are two available electrons per bond—just the right number for *saturated bonding* with no electron deficiency. In the crystal of metallic sodium, on the

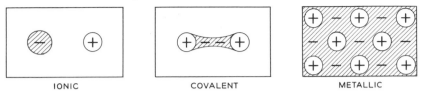

| IONIC | COVALENT | METALLIC |

FIGURE 21 – MEMORY AIDS *for three extreme types of bonding. Most actual bonds are not pure, but are formed by some mixture of these types.*

other hand, there are eight neighbors and one available electron per atom. Thus there are four bonds per atom and only one-quarter electron per bond; the electron deficiency is one and three-quarters per bond.

Why Metals Conduct Well

The fact that the electrons in a metal can move quite freely from atom to atom explains the high electrical conductivity of metals. They are *electronic conductors*, which conduct electricity by the motion of relatively free *electrons*, unlike a salt solution which conducts electricity by the motion of free *ions*. In solid salt the ions cannot move freely because they are much bulkier than electrons and are packed together tightly, and the crystal is an insulator. But when salt is melted, the ions can move past one another, and the molten material becomes a good *ionic conductor.*

The freedom of the electrons to move in a metal makes them behave in some ways very much like the atoms in a gas. But you can pick out immediately two conspicuous differences between an "electron gas" and an atomic gas. In the first place, the electron gas is compressed into a much smaller space than the atomic gas. In sodium, with one free electron per atom, there are as many electrons as atoms in a given amount of space. The electron gas is compressed as much as an atomic gas which has been squeezed down to one thousandth of its normal volume.

In the second place, each electron bears a negative charge, unlike the atoms in a gas. The electrons are all repelling one another and trying to stay out of one another's way. And they have left behind them their parent atoms, which have thus become positive ions. One physicist has likened a metal to "a collection of positively charged raisins in a negatively charged cake." The electrostatic attraction between the raisins and the cake holds the entire assembly together.

You may find that it is helpful to carry a little symbolic picture in your mind, summarizing the ideas about the several types of bonding that we have discussed. With the reminder that its pictures must be understood in terms of the preceding discussions, Figure 21 offers aids for recalling the meaning of the "ionic" bond, the "covalent" bond, and the "metallic" bond.

Is Salt a Metal?

Return now to examine a little further the idea of *electron deficient bonding*, by applying to sodium chloride the arithmetic described earlier in this chapter. In a crystal of sodium chloride each atom has six nearest neighbors of the other species, as Figure 16 shows. The arithmetic gives three bonds per atom. A sodium atom has one electron in its outermost occupied shell, and a chlorine atom has seven. The arithmetic gives four electrons per atom. Hence there are four-thirds electrons per bond. Common salt, with an election deficiency of two thirds, should be a metal — a shiny conductor of electricity, not the white insulating powder that seasons our food.

It will not avail to say that sodium chloride is an ionic crystal, and the arithmetic was designed to deal only with covalent and metallic crystals. Few bonds are "pure"; most bonding displays a mixture of the three types that we discussed. The actual world presents no clear borderline between ionic bonding on the one hand, and covalent and metallic bonding on the other. To comfort yourself by saying, "It's still all right because sodium chloride is an ionic crystal," brings you close to indulging in the fallacy of assuming what you set out to prove.

Notice, however, that the examples — diamond and sodium — in which the arithmetic worked successfully are materials made of atoms of a single species, whereas sodium chloride is made of two species. This suggests that, in applying the idea of electron-deficient bonding and its associated arithmetic to solid matter, you might do well to speak only of crystals of the elements. This is a tight restriction, to be sure, but a necessary one.

Notice also that you must know the arrangement of atoms in the crystal that you are talking about before you can apply the arithmetic to solids. Only by knowing that arrangement can you count the number of nearest neighbors of each atom, and thus the number of bonds per atom. If the carbon atoms in a diamond took the same arrangement as the sodium atoms in a crystal of

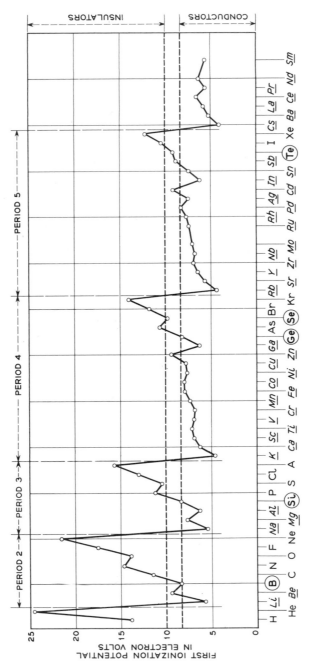

FIGURE 22—THE FIRST IONIZATION POTENTIAL of an atomic species is the smallest energy required to remove an electron from an atom. Plotted for the species in order of their listing in the Periodic Table they form another instance of the periodicity displayed in that table. The highest energies are required for the rare gases, the lowest for the alkali metals. Every species for which this quantity exceeds 10 e.v. forms an electrically insulating solid, and every species for which the quantity is less than 8 e.v. forms an electrically conducting solid. Between these values fall some conductors (underlined) and some semiconductors (circled).

sodium, each would have eight nearest neighbors instead of four, each bond would be a one-electron bond, and there would be an electron deficiency of one per bond instead of the saturated bonding that you actually find in a diamond.

Ionization Potentials

It would be helpful to discover, by studying the properties of the various species of atoms, some criterion that would decide whether those atoms would choose to arrange themselves in a way that leaves their bonding with an electron deficiency. A little further thought about what happens to the electrons in these bonds will help to suggest such a criterion.

In a diamond, for example, each electron stays at home, for the most part—remaining in the electron-pair bond to which it belongs. In metals, on the other hand, the electrons stray from atom to atom. But when an electron strays, it removes itself from one bond and drops into another. To remove an electron from a bond takes energy. Clearly it must take more energy to remove an electron from the bond in diamond than from the bond in a metal.

Now go on to relate the energy required to break a bond with the properties of the atoms that are engaging in the bond. When two atoms establish a bond, at least one bonding electron wanders between those two atoms. The bonding electron is derived originally from one of the atoms, and it wanders only because its energy will be lower if it wanders than if it stays in its parent atom. But, looking at one species of atoms after another, you might expect that the two energies—of the electron in an atom and the electron in a bond—would go up and down together.

This reasoning suggests looking at the energy required to remove one electron from the outermost occupied shell of an atom —the shell containing the electrons that engage in bonding. That energy, called the *first ionization potential*, has been experimentally measured for almost all species of atoms; the results are plotted in Figure 22. There the elements are listed horizontally in the order of their listing in the Periodic Table (Table IV). The energy required to remove one electron from the uppermost occupied energy level in each of those atoms is plotted vertically. The chosen unit of energy is the *electron volt* (abbreviated to e.v.), a unit that is often used in atomic problems. One electron volt is the kinetic energy that will be acquired by an electron when it is accelerated through a potential difference of one volt; it is equal to 1.6×10^{-12} erg.

Proceeding through Figure 22 and identifying the atomic species that form metals and those that don't, you will find that there is a fairly definite dividing line running horizontally through the diagram. In other words, at the atomic separations found in solids, the neighboring nuclei seem to be able to exert about the same amount of force on one another's electrons, no matter what species they belong to. If the electrons need more than that to escape, they will not be free to conduct electricity.

In short, it is possible to put up a picture of electron-deficient bonding in metals, which holds together in consistent fashion. It is, so to speak, a "chemical" picture. The next chapter puts up a more "physical" picture, and pursues some of its consequences in analyzing the conduction of electricity by metals. But it would be a pity to think of these pictures as distinct. After all, the metal is the same metal in both pictures, and physics and chemistry really form a single science.

5 Charge Carriers in Solids

Agreed: an electric current is a flow of electric charges. A current can flow, therefore, only where there are charges, and where those charges are free to flow. All matter contains electric charges; they reside on the nuclei and electrons of which we believe the matter is made. It remains to describe the circumstances in which they can flow through the matter that contains them. Why did the electric charges flow so much more easily through Stephen Gray's brass wire than through his silk thread?

A good place to start thinking about this problem is to look again at solutions of salts — at the electrolyses described in Chapter 2 from which Michael Faraday derived such a revealing body of information. In those solutions, as Arrhenius concluded, oppositely charged ions are swimming independently. Under the electrical force applied to them by the charges on the electrodes, the positive ions drift toward the negatively charged electrode, and the negatively charged ions toward the positively charged electrode. Since opposite charges moving in opposite directions correspond with electric currents in the *same* direction, the total current is the sum of the currents carried by the two species of ions. Thus the charge carriers in a solution of common salt are sodium ions (positively charged because each neutral sodium atom has lost one electron) and chloride ions (negatively charged because each neutral chlorine atom has acquired one of the electrons lost by the sodium atoms).

Why Solid Salt Is Not a Conductor

Now, unlike the solution, a crystal of sodium chloride is a fairly good insulator. And yet, as Figure 16 showed, the crystal is made of ions, not of neutral atoms. Since the crystal contains the same charge carriers as the solution, the fact that it conducts electricity poorly may seem puzzling at first. But a glance at the

65

right side of Figure 16 makes clear that the ions are packed together so tightly in the crystal that they are not free to move past
one another.

In other words, a salt crystal is an electrical insulator, not because it contains no charge carriers but because they are not free
to move. To be sure, those ions are vibrating with the heat vibrations in which the atoms of any piece of matter participate. But
in the crystal they are constrained by their neighbors to vibrate
about fixed positions. As the temperature is increased, the ampli-

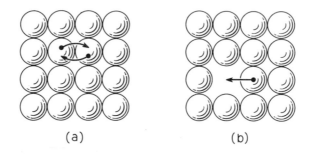

(a)   (b)

FIGURE 23 – INTERCHANGING TWO ATOMS *in a crystal (a) is very difficult*
because the atoms must acquire a very high energy to squeeze past each other.
An atom and a vacancy (b) can interchange positions relatively easily.

tude of those vibrations increases, until finally the ions knock
one another far enough apart to move past one another. Abruptly
the crystal melts, and equally abruptly the material becomes a
good electrical conductor.

This argument explains very well why an ionic crystal is a
poor conductor of electricity. In fact this argument does its job
too well; an ionic crystal is indeed a good insulator, but it is
not a perfect insulator. A new question arises: How can the
crystal conduct the little trickle of current that is able to leak
through it?

Vacancies in Crystals

The answer to that question that is accepted today for most
cases is suggested in Figure 23. An atom must acquire so much
kinetic energy to squeeze through the space between its neighbors that the event happens rarely if ever at ordinary temperature. But if there are *vacancies* in the crystal—atomic sites that
are unoccupied by atoms—an atom adjacent to a vacancy can

squeeze into that vacancy relatively easily. By doing so, it leaves a new vacancy—the site that it previously occupied. Thus ion after ion can shift, conducting electric current by the relay race in which they engage.

There is other evidence, apart from their electrical conductivities, that crystals embody vacancies in their atomic arrangements. And that fact may not surprise you when you remember how any crystal is formed. A crystal does not spring into being all at once; it grows. In the course of their excursions in a solution or a molten material, a few atoms happen to arrange themselves in the proper crystalline order. Then, if conditions are favorable, the atoms that meet the surfaces of the little incipient crystal attach themselves to it and propagate the same order outward.

It is important to visualize how fast this must occur in the usual act of solidification. A crystal is growing "very slowly" if its faces advance at the rate of one-eighth inch every day. But even in that "slow" growth, more than a hundred newly ordered layers of atoms must be laid down on the surface during each second of time. In the hustle and bustle of atoms finding their right positions, it would be too much to ask that they do not occasionally leave vacant a suitable site.

There is a useful abstract picture of ionic conduction assisted by vacancies. If a site that should be occupied is not occupied by an ion, then an electric charge is missing from a neighborhood that would be electrically neutral only if the site were occupied. In other words, the neighborhood of the vacancy is left with a net charge equal and opposite to that of the missing ion. When an ion squeezes into the vacancy, leaving behind it a new vacancy, neutrality is restored where the old vacancy used to be. But now the newly vacated site is surrounded by the same net charge.

Thus you can think of the vacancy as if it were a "charged particle," whose charge is opposite to that of the missing ion and which moves in the opposite direction from the ion that squeezes into it. That "particle" is fictitious, of course—an abstraction. The abstraction is useful because it enables you to think of "conduction by vacancies"—by the drift of a few "particles" through the crystal instead of by a complicated relay race of many ions, as Figure 24 shows. You will find use for a similar abstraction in thinking about semiconductors in later chapters of this book.

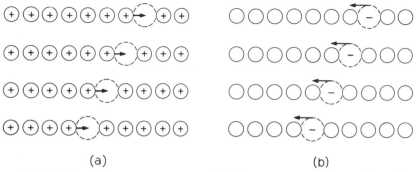

(a)   (b)

FIGURE 24 – IONIC CONDUCTION, *assisted by a vacancy in a crystal, can be visualized either (a) as the successive motions of many positively charged particles, each through a short distance, or better (b) as the continued motion of one negatively charged vacancy in the opposite direction through a long distance.*

Turn now to examine the great contrast between electrical conduction in ionic crystals and in metals. Their conductivities differ by a staggering factor, a million million million million. A trickle of current through an ionic crystal is accompanied by a transport of matter; a relatively enormous current through a metal seems to transport no matter. "The electric matter," said Benjamin Franklin in 1756, "consists of particles extremely subtle, since it can permeate common matter, even the densest, with such freedom and ease as not to receive any appreciable resistance."

Nobody seems to have made use of Franklin's remarkable insight until 1875, when Wilhelm Weber tried to put up a more exact picture of how Franklin's "subtle particles" might conduct electricity through a metal. Weber imagined that a metal was made of molecules that were not completely stable and contained electrically charged particles in constant motion. He suggested that those molecules are unstable, that charged particles leave them from time to time, and that each particle that escapes is urged by any applied electromotive force to move through the metal until another molecule captures it. Then the recaptured particle participates in the motion of the capturing molecule until it is ejected again.

Drude's Theory of Metallic Conduction

But any such speculation had to remain poorly founded until Thomson identified the electron, as Chapter 2 narrated. Promptly several investigators attempted to make tenable theories of metallic conduction in which electrons played the parts of Franklin's "subtle particles." In 1900 Paul Drude published the most successful of these attempts. Even though it has since been superseded by the wave-mechanical theory of electrons in metals, Drude's picture remains useful, and his method of analysis introduces many of the ideas that later theories employ.

Notice, in the first place, two important quantitative ideas that must be made precise in any theory that sets out to explain electrical conduction. Surely, the more carriers of electricity are at hand, the more electricity can be conducted. But surely the number of charge carriers cannot be the only determining factor. For example, molten sodium chloride is made of ions that are all free to move about: It has one carrier per atom. In solid metallic sodium, each atom presumably contributes its one outermost electron to the electron-deficient bonding described in Chapter 4: Again, there is one carrier per atom. But the conductivity of metallic sodium is a million times greater than the conductivity

DRUDE

PAUL KARL LUDWIG DRUDE (1863-1906) *was born at Brunswick, Germany, and studied at Göttingen, Freiburg, and Berlin. In 1894 he became extraordinary professor of physics at Leipzig, and in 1900 he moved to Giessen as professor of physics.*

The six years at Leipzig were especially fruitful for Drude. There he pursued the application of the electromagnetic theory of light, which had been put forward by James Clerk Maxwell in 1865, to several problems of the interaction between light and matter. He developed detailed theories of the optical behavior of metals, the variation of the amount of refraction by a substance with the wavelength of the refracted light, and the magneto-optical phenomena of iron, nickel, and cobalt. During this period Drude also wrote two treatises well known to physicists, which passed through many German editions and were translated into English, "The Physics of the Aether" and "A Treatise on Optics."

When Drude moved to Giessen he also took over the editorship of the famous German scientific journal, "Annalen der Physik," which Gustav Wiedemann had edited for twenty-two years until his death in 1899. It was in Giessen that Drude also constructed his theory of the behavior of free electrons in metals, described in Chapters 5 and 6. In 1905 he became professor of physics at Berlin, but a year later Drude killed himself.

of molten sodium chloride. In short, when you have answered the question, "How many carriers are there?" you must still answer, "How easily can each carrier slide through the material?"

Drude's reasoning went somewhat as follows: Suppose that the electrons in a metal are free to move about among the ions that they have left behind them. They might behave much like the atoms in a gas—a dense gas containing the ions as obstacles. Then they dash about among these ions, colliding with them fairly frequently and consequently taking very jagged and irregular courses.

When an electron collides with an ion, it sometimes gives some of its kinetic energy to the ion, and at other times it gains some kinetic energy because the ion is vibrating. On the whole, an electron gains energy as frequently as it loses energy, and it gains or loses velocity in any direction equally often. At equilibrium, all these gains and losses balance out.

But these balances are upset when an electrical force is applied to the electrons from outside. Then, between collisions, each electron accelerates in the direction of the force, gaining some velocity in that direction during its time of free flight, as Figure 25 suggests. On the average, therefore, a little more charge is moving in that direction than in any other. That bit of extra velocity, multiplied by the magnitude of the charge on an electron, is the electric current that the electric force produces. Figure 26 shows how to put these ideas into a quantitative expression for that current.

The argument now advances to show how the extra velocity, which is responsible for the electric current, depends on the electric force. Clearly, if the collisions of the electrons with the

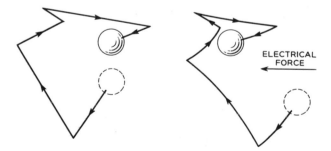

ELECTRICAL
FORCE

FIGURE 25 – A FREE ELECTRON *in a metal is traveling at a high speed and bouncing off the atoms, tracing an irregular path (left). When an electrical force is applied from outside, the force adds a slight directed drift to the electron's irregular motion (right).*

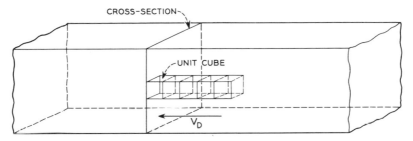

FIGURE 26 – THE ELECTRIC CURRENT *through any cross section of a metal is the amount of charge transported through that cross section per second. It is most convenient to calculate the* current density, j – *the current passing through each unit area of the cross section. Then the total current will be given by j times the area of the cross section. As shown above, the current density will be the total number of charge carriers per unit volume* (N) *times the charge on each carrier* (−e) *times the average excess velocity* (V_D) *of the carriers, or* $j = NeV_D$. *The subscript "D" refers to the fact that the average excess velocity is often called the* drift velocity. *Thus, in one second, V_D of the unit cubes of electric charge pass from left to right through a unit area of the cross section.*

ions did not affect that extra velocity, then the longer the electric force acted the larger the extra velocity would grow. The force would keep accelerating the electrons in its own direction.

But the current through a metal stays constant so long as the electric force stays constant; it does not increase with the length of time the force is applied. You are obliged to suppose that the electrons somehow lose that extra velocity every once in a while, and then pick it up again. In other words, every once in a while an electron collides with an ion in a particular way – in a way such that the electron loses its extra velocity. Collisions of this sort, in which a particle loses all memory of what the forces have done to it in the past, are sometimes called *effective collisions*.

Imagine that after an effective collision an electron has no extra velocity in the direction of the electric force. The force then accelerates it uniformly until it has another effective collision. If its velocity is zero at the beginning of this trip, its average velocity during the trip is just half the velocity it finally attains at the end of the trip, as Figure 27 shows.

Applying Newton's Second Law

We can find out what that final velocity is by using Newton's second law of motion. That law says that the force on the electron equals its mass times its acceleration. The force is given by the

■ EXCESS VELOCITY ■

The final excess velocity picked up by a charge carrier from an applied electric force between its effective collisions is obedient to Newton's second law of motion:

$$F = ma.$$

The force, F, on the carrier is given by the force per unit charge, E, times the charge on the carrier, $-e$:

$$F = -eE.$$

The acceleration of the carrier, a, is given by its final velocity, V_F, divided by the time required to reach that velocity, t:

$$a = \frac{V_F}{t}.$$

Thus Newton's second law for this particular case becomes

$$-eE = m\frac{V_F}{t},$$

which yields the final velocity when both sides are multiplied by t/m:

$$V_F = \frac{-eEt}{m}.$$

Then the drift velocity, shown in Figure 27 to be one half the final velocity, is given by

$$V_D = \frac{-eEt}{2m}.$$

■ CURRENT DENSITY ■

Ohm's Law, which states that the current through a metal is proportional to the force that drives it, can be "derived" by substituting our new expression for V_D into the equation derived in Figure 26:

$$j = -NeV_D.$$

The result shows that the current density, j, is proportional to the electric force per unit charge, E:

$$j = \frac{Ne^2t}{2m}E.$$

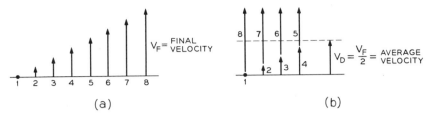

FIGURE 27 – EXCESS VELOCITY *is picked up by the carriers during their flight between "effective collisions." Since the electric force accelerates each carrier at a uniform rate between those collisions, the velocity of the carrier increases uniformly from zero (just after a collision) up to a final value (just before the next collision), as shown in (a) for successive numbered instants. Then the average excess velocity can be found by the device of averaging pairs of instantaneous velocities. Choosing the members of each pair properly, the average for each pair is the same—namely one half the final velocity—as shown in (b). Thus the drift velocity, V_D of Figure 26, turns out to be half the final velocity, V_F.*

potential difference per unit length in the metal, times the charge on the electron, as Figure 4 made clear. And since the acceleration is uniform during the trip, it is given by the difference in the velocities at the beginning and end of the trip, divided by the time taken to make the trip.

Of course the time taken by an electron to make such a trip will vary from one trip to another. In order to simplify matters, it is convenient to use a single time—the average time taken by all such electrons to make all such trips, called the *mean free time* of an electron. These bits and pieces can now be put into Newton's second law, to get a quantitative expression for the average extra velocity of the electrons that is given to them by the electric force. (See "Excess Velocity" on page 72.)

Current Density and Conductivity

At this point in the argument, you hold in your hands two quantitative expressions. One gives the density of the electric current through a metal in terms of the average excess velocity of the mobile electrons in the metal (Figure 26). The other, which we have just derived, gives that average excess velocity in terms of the electric force that produces it. By combining the two, as in "Current Density" on page 72, you can get what you were looking for, an expression for the current density in terms of the electric force.

This expression has two especially noteworthy features. In the first place, it says that the current through any particular

■ Conductivity ■

The conductivity of a metal can be expressed in terms of the properties of the charge carriers in the metal by using the new form of Ohm's Law that we have derived. By comparing the usual form of the law,

$$j = \sigma E,$$

with the newly derived form,

$$j = \frac{Ne^2 t}{2m} E,$$

we can see that the conductivity, σ, is given by

$$\sigma = \frac{Ne^2 t}{2m}.$$

Thus the conductivity is proportional to the density of mobile electrons, N, and to their mean free time, t, in the material.

---

metal is proportional to the applied voltage. In other words, it "derives" Ohm's Law. In the second place, looking back at Figure 4, you see that this new way of writing Ohm's Law gives you an expression for the *conductivity* of a material in terms of the behavior of the particles that compose it (see "Conductivity" above).

It is worthwhile to examine this new expression for the conductivity narrowly to see what is in it. Begin by dividing it into three parts:

$$\sigma = (Ne)\left(\frac{e}{2m}\right)(t).$$

The first part, Ne, says that the amount of charge transported is proportional to the charge density — the amount of mobile charge in a unit volume of the material. The second part, $e/2m$, says that the acceleration which a voltage can give to any of the charge carriers is proportional to the magnitude of the charge on the carrier and inversely proportional to its mass. The third part, t, says that the voltage can accelerate the carrier only during one mean free time; when it has an effective collision, the carrier loses all memory of what the voltage did to it earlier.

All the ideas embodied in this expression seem quantitatively reasonable. Indeed you would expect to find an expression looking much like this for the conductivity of any material — gas, liquid, or solid. Just two quantities distinguish one material from another—N, the number of charge carriers per unit volume, and t, their mean free time.*

Usually it is possible to make a good "educated guess" at the value of N. For example, Chapter 4 described the grounds for believing that metallic sodium has one mobile electron per atom. Then the number of mobile electrons per unit volume can be calculated by simple arithmetic.

But there is no easy way to guess the mean free time of a charge carrier in a material. Instead, using its measured conductivity and the conjectured density of charge carriers in it, you can turn the expression for the conductivity around and calculate the value of the mean free time. Then any proposed theory of conduction must yield a value of the mean free time that agrees reasonably well with that "measured value." The next chapter describes some efforts to accomplish that task.

---

* In comparing the formulas of this chapter with similar formulas for conductivity derived in other places, you may be confused by one apparent discrepancy. In more recent treatments of the problem, carried out by more advanced methods, the "mean free time" is usually defined in such a way that it has one half the value of the mean free time used here. Hence the formulas will differ by a factor of two, or one half.

6 The Effects of Heat on Conductors

Two centuries of patient labor by unnumbered investigators lay between Stephen Gray's observations of electrical conduction and Paul Drude's effort to explain how metals conduct. And the many experiments carried out through those centuries — only a few of which are described in the preceding chapters — slowly painted a picture. Each of the atoms composing the metal contributes a negatively charged electron to a common pool, and thereby becomes a positively charged ion. The ions are held together by the attraction of the pool, and the pool is prevented from escaping by the attraction of the ions.

Electron Gas

The word "pool," however, connotes a liquid; more usually the mobile electrons are said to form an *electron gas*. To be sure, that gas is very much condensed, in comparison with familiar gases — condensed to about one thousandth of the volume that a gas of the same number of atoms would occupy at the same temperature and pressure. Its volume corresponds closely with a liquid, not a gas. But the electrons are pictured as moving about freely, without feeling attractions from one another as the atoms in a liquid do. In fact, far from feeling attracted, they are repelled by one another's negative charges.

In the simplest picture of an electron gas, these repulsions between the electrons, and the attractions of the ions for the electrons, are all neglected. The positive charge of the ions and the negative charge of the electrons are smeared out in the metal, neutralizing each other. Then the electrons can be treated as uncharged particles, except in their function of transporting charge in an electric current; and the ions can be treated as uncharged obstacles to the electrons' motions, except in their function of preventing the electron gas from escaping.

Accepting this picture of an electron gas pervading a metal, Paul Drude developed the ideas described in Chapter 5. When he noticed the crucial importance of the mean free time of the electrons between their effective collisions with the ions, he went on to see whether he could make a theory of the mean free time by using the kinetic theory of ordinary gases. In this effort, Drude was able to build upon the results of a century of investigations by others into the nature of *heat*.

RUMFORD

BENJAMIN THOMPSON, COUNT RUMFORD (1753-1814) *is variously described as scientist, philanthropist, administrator, opportunist, spy, and traitor. In a recent account of Sir Ernest Rutherford's life and work, E. N. da Costa Andrade has encapsulated in the following words "that remarkable figure Count Rumford, born in America as Benjamin Thompson, who joined the British ranks in Boston in 1775 and in 1776 left his native land, never to return. He was appointed to a comfortable post in London, and while there engaged in scientific experiments and was made a Fellow of the Royal Society. Later he went to Bavaria, where he reorganized the army and carried out with extraordinary success the task of reducing to contented order a rabble of beggars and vagabonds who were terrorizing Munich. He expressed his principles in the words, 'To make vicious and abandoned people happy it has generally been supposed necessary first to make them virtuous. But why not reverse the order? Why not make them happy, and then virtuous?' For his services to Bavaria, where incidentally he made important observations on the nature of heat which are recorded in most textbooks of physics, he was made a count of the Holy Roman Empire and assumed the title of Count Rumford. Rumford was the name by which Concord, New Hampshire, where he spent decisive years of his early manhood, was originally known. Later he returned to England, where he was instrumental in founding the Royal Institution. Finally he went to France, where, to his great discomfort, he married the wealthy widow of the famous French chemist, Antoine Laurent Lavoisier, executed during the French Revolution."*

Rumford's anecdotal introductions to his scientific papers remind us again of the casual origins of much scientific discovery. "When dining, I had often observed that some particular dishes retained their Heat much longer than others; and that apple pies, and apples and almonds mixed (a dish in great repute in England) remained hot a surprising length of time. Much struck with this extraordinary quality of retaining Heat, which apples appeared to possess, it frequently occurred to my recollection; and I never burnt my mouth with them, or saw others meet with the same misfortune, without endeavoring, but in vain, to find out some way of accounting, in a satisfactory manner, for this surprising phenomenon." And he undertook experiments leading to the picture of the transfer of heat by convection.

Heat as Molecular Motion

In earlier days it had seemed natural to suppose that the heat which flows from a hot to a cold body is some unique kind of substance. But about the year 1800 many experiments, especially those of Benjamin Thompson, Count Rumford, verified earlier guesses that the heat in hot bodies is in fact associated with a mode of motion—a disorganized random motion of the bodies' constituent molecules. We now visualize the heating of a cold body as an excitation of its molecules to a more vigorous motion by the impacts of the more vigorously moving molecules in the

JOULE

JAMES PRESCOTT JOULE (1818-1889) *was born in Manchester, England, and received early instruction there in chemistry from John Dalton, the major proponent of the modern atomic theory of matter. But most of his scientific knowledge was self-taught, especially his understanding of electricity and magnetism.*

When he was 19 years old, Joule invented an electromagnetic engine. Attempting to study its performance quantitatively, he was frustrated by the vague methods then common for specifying electrical quantities. Faraday's quantitative work on electrolysis suggested to him, as a convenient unit of electrical current, the amount required to decompose nine grains of water in an hour. Thus he was enabled to make in 1840 a quantitative statement of the law by which an electric current produces heat in an electrical conductor.

Joule's concern for exact measurement persisted throughout his work, and led to the achievement for which he is most famous. As early as 1843 he stated his conviction that, when mechanical force is expended, an exact equivalent of heat is always obtained. Doggedly and with his best care Joule made a series of determinations of the mechanical equivalent of heat over the next six years. One sort of determination was made by forcing water through capillary tubes, another by compressing air, and still another by stirring water with a paddle wheel. Much later he returned to the problem, this time by measuring the thermal effects of electrical currents. Ultimately he brought the determinations by various methods into agreement, establishing the value 772.55 foot-pounds as the work required to raise the temperature of one pound of water from 60° to 61° Fahrenheit.

Joule also studied the thermal changes in solids when they are stretched or compressed longitudinally, and in gases when they are compressed and when they are forced through small apertures. The latter study led him to make the important suggestion of the steam condenser for improving the efficiency of steam engines.

hot body. Both the heat that flows and the temperature differences that urge it to flow can be identified with aspects of those molecular motions.

During the first half of the Nineteenth Century it became steadily clearer that the heat absorbed by matter is precisely equivalent to the *energy* associated with the motion of the atoms in the matter. About the middle of that century James Joule established the amount of energy that is equivalent to one *calorie*, often called "the mechanical equivalent of heat."

Meanwhile, there had been accumulating a body of experimental results on how gases behave when their pressure and temperature is varied. As early as 1660, Robert Boyle had investigated the "doctrine of the spring of the air." His work, over-

BOYLE

ROBERT BOYLE (1627-1691) *was born at Lismore Castle, Ireland, the fourteenth child of the Great Earl of Cork. Learning to speak Latin and French as a child, entering Eton at the age of eight, he was clearly precocious. After three years at Eton, he went abroad to travel with a French tutor and spent two years in Geneva. Soon he was in Italy and spent a winter in Florence studying the "paradoxes of the great star-gazer" Galileo, who died the following year. Returning to England, he found that his father's death had left him with a comfortable income, and he devoted his life to scientific and theological study.*

Boyle soon took a prominent place in the "Invisible College," a band of inquirers into the "new philosophy" who met in London and Oxford. While living at Oxford he read of Otto von Guericke's air-pump and joined with Robert Hooke in improving its construction. With the resulting "pneumatical engine" he carried out the experiments measuring the relationship between the pressure and the volume of a gas, mentioned on page 82.

In 1663 the "Invisible College" became the Royal Society of London, to whose council Boyle was named in the charter granted by Charles II. Like other early members of that society, Boyle joyfully traversed many fields of interest—specific gravities, optical refraction, crystals, electricity, color, hydrostatics, the chemistry of combustion and respiration—and he was the first to discover the part played by air in the propagation of sound. His scriptural studies also were extensive; he learned Hebrew, Greek, and Syriac in order to pursue them. He founded by his will the Boyle lectures for proving the Christian religion against "notorious infidels," stipulating, however, that controversies between Christians should not be mentioned.

JOSEPH LOUIS GAY-LUSSAC (1778-1850) *is best known to most people by "Gay-Lussac's Law," cited on page 81. But in the paper describing his experiments and his deductions from them, Gay-Lussac generously points out that "Citizen Charles noticed the same property of these gases fifteen years ago; but never having published his results, it is only by the greatest accident that I have come to know of them."*

GAY-LUSSAC

Gay-Lussac's position in science, how-ever, does not rest exclusively, or even prin-cipally, on that work. For him,. as for most of his contemporaries, physics and chemistry formed a single science, and his efforts ranged over both. Indeed for many years he served as professor of chemistry at the École Polytechnique, and at the same time as professor of physics at the Sorbonne.

As a young man Gay-Lussac showed a taste for physical adventure unusually bold for a scientist. When he was twenty-six he made two balloon ascensions, reaching an altitude of 23,000 feet, to investigate how the earth's magnetic field varies with altitude; and he used that opportunity to measure also the temperature and humidity of the high-altitude air and to collect samples of it. He found no variation with altitude in either the magnetic field or the atmospheric composition. In the following year he made a "scientific journey" through Switzerland, Italy, and Germany, visiting Mount Vesuvius when that volcano was in full eruption.

Turning to more strictly chemical investigations later, he found him-self paralleling the path of Sir Humphry Davy, and occasionally the two men came into direct rivalry. Davy's electrical method for preparing metallic potassium spurred Gay-Lussac and Louis Thénard to develop a purely chemical method; in 1808 they succeeded in reducing potash by red-hot iron, and soon afterward they used the newly isolated metal to reduce boric acid to boron. In a controversy with Davy over the nature of "oxymuriatic acid," or chlorine, Gay-Lussac was less fortu-nate: After many experiments he concluded that chlorine is an oxygen-bearing compound, and only later accepted Davy's conclusion that it is an elementary substance. A few years later he was wise enough to adopt Davy's opinion that iodine is elementary also, and went on to make an elaborate study of the properties of that newly isolated element.

As time passed, Gay-Lussac's eminence brought him increasing responsibilities as an adviser on the technical problems of French in-dustry and government. Characteristically he introduced scientific methods and measurements into areas previously acquainted only with practical approximations. He improved processes for manufacturing sulfuric acid and oxalic acid, and for determining the amount of alkali in commercial potash and soda and the available chlorine in bleaching powder. During his last years, as assayer to the mint, he standardized methods for assaying silver.

looked at the time, was duplicated by Edme Mariotte independently sixteen years later. Mariotte concluded that "we can take as a fixed rule or law of nature that air is condensed in proportion to the weight with which it is loaded." In other words — the words used by Louis-Joseph Gay-Lussac almost 150 years later: "all gases . . . occupy volumes which are inversely proportional to the weights which compress them."

Bernouilli's Mental Model of a Gas

The year 1738 saw the publication of an extraordinary experiment — an experiment of a purely intellectual kind. On the basis of the growing belief that matter is ultimately made of innumerable tiny particles, Daniel Bernouilli made a mental "model" of a gas. His writing, now more than two centuries old, speaks almost as a contemporary theoretical physicist would speak.

"Consider a cylindrical vessel ACDB [Figure 28] set vertically, and a movable piston EF in it, on which is placed a weight *P*: Let the cavity ECDF contain very minute corpuscles, which are driven hither and thither with a very rapid motion; so that these corpuscles, when they strike against the piston EF and sustain it by their repeated impacts, form an elastic fluid which will expand of itself if the weight *P* is removed or diminished, which will be condensed if the weight is increased, and which gravitates toward the horizontal bottom CD just as if it were endowed with no elastic powers: For whether the corpuscles are at rest or are agitated they do not lose their weight, so that the bottom sus-

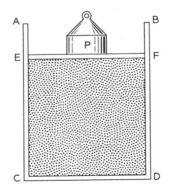

FIGURE 28 – BERNOUILLI'S PICTURE *of a gas corresponds closely with today's. "Very minute corpuscles," in rapid motion, strike the movable piston EF, and their impacts sustain the weight P.*

tains not only the weight but the elasticity of the fluid. Such therefore is the fluid which we shall substitute for air."

Using the mechanical principles obeyed by ordinary visible particles, Bernouilli calculated how his "gas" of invisible particles should behave, and compared his results with the experimental findings of Boyle and Mariotte. "From all the facts known we may conclude that natural air can be very much condensed and compressed into a practically infinitely small space." After citing this fact to justify neglecting the sizes of the particles in his formulas, Bernouilli deduced that, for his model, "the compressing weights are almost in the inverse ratio of the spaces which air occupies when compressed by different amounts."

DANIEL BERNOUILLI (1700-1782) *was a distinguished member of an incredibly distinguished family. In his study, "Hereditary Genius," Francis Galton points out that "no fewer than 120 of the descendants of the mathematical Bernouillis have been traced genealogically . . . the majority achieved distinction . . . none were failures." Daniel's father Jean and his uncle Jacques, brilliant mathematicians both, made their home in Basel, Switzerland, but Daniel was born in the Netherlands city of Groningen during his father's tenyear stay there as professor of mathematics.*

BERNOUILLI

Galton adds that the Bernouillis were mostly "quarrelsome and unamiable." Violence, abuse and jealousy marked this tough breed; Jean did everything possible to turn Daniel from mathematics, mistreating him as a child and trying to force him into business when he grew older. Daniel studied medicine and became a physician, but at the age of 25 he accepted an appointment as professor of mathematics at Saint Petersburg, Russia. Returning to Basel in 1733, he became professor of anatomy, of botany, and finally of "experimental and speculative philosophy" — of "physics," as we would say today. Soon he won a prize from the French Academy of Sciences that his father coveted, and Jean threw him out of the house.

In his most famous work, the "Hydrodynamica" published in 1738, Bernouilli laid the theoretical and practical foundations for the "equilibrium, pressure, reaction, and varied velocities" of fluids, and its tenth section contains the initiation of the kinetic theory of gases quoted on page 81. He continued his creative work until he was 80, concerning himself with matters thrown up by the problems of navigation, astronomy, the tides, and the vibration of cords. At the last he was especially interested in the practical application of the "doctrine of probabilities," particularly to economics.

But Bernouilli did not content himself with this use of his model. Having explained the observations that relate the pressure and the volume of a gas, he went on to suggest how heating a gas increases its pressure if its volume is held constant. "The elasticity of air is not only increased by condensation but by heat supplied to it, and since it is admitted that heat may be considered as an increasing internal motion of the particles, it follows that, if the elasticity of air of which the volume does not change is increased, this indicates a more intense motion in the particles of air; which fits in well with our hypothesis; for it is plain that so much the greater weight *P* is needed to keep the air in the condition ECDF, as the aerial particles are agitated by the greater velocity. It is not difficult to see that the weight *P* should be in the duplicate ratio of this velocity because, when the velocity increases, not only the number of impacts but also the intensity of each of them increases equally, and each of them is proportional to the weight *P*."

In the language of our time, the phrase, "in the duplicate ratio," means "proportional to the square." Bernouilli was suggesting that the pressure of a gas held at constant volume is proportional to the square of the velocity of its particles.

The Gas Laws

Armed with the experimental results of Boyle and Mariotte, and with the brilliant insights of Bernouilli, we are equipped to bypass a century of further work on gases. Using our own heads, we can leap to many of the conclusions available to Drude for making a theory of the behavior of the electron gas in a metal.

In the first place, the law connecting the pressure and the volume of a gas states that the volume is inversely proportional to the pressure. But clearly the volume must also depend on how much gas you are examining. If you examine a great many different gases, all at the same temperature and pressure, it turns out that their volumes are all the same when you choose amounts of these gases that are in the same proportion as their molecular weights. In other words, the volume occupied by a given number of molecules of a gas, at a given temperature and pressure, is the same for all species of molecules. For example, if the amount of gas that you examine is one *gram-molecule* (the chemists' molecular weight expressed in grams) and the pressure and temperature are "normal" (the pressure supports a column of

■ BOYLE'S LAW FOR GASES ■

Boyle's Law, often called in Europe the Law of Mariotte, says that the volume, V, of a gas is inversely proportional to its pressure, p. Of course, its volume is also proportional to its total amount, which can be summarized by the number n of gram-molecules. Thus we have

$$V = \frac{Kn}{p}.$$

Multiplying both sides of this expression by p yields the more usual way of writing the law:

$$pV = nK.$$

---

mercury 76 centimeters tall, and the temperature is 20 degrees centigrade), then the volume of any gas is 22.4 liters.

You can now write an expression such as that derived in "Boyle's Law for Gases" above. This says that the volume, V, of any gas is directly proportional to the number, n, of gram-molecules of the gas and inversely proportional to its pressure, p. And you can argue that the constant of proportionality, K, cannot depend on the pressure, because the pressure is already taken care of in the formula. Moreover, it cannot depend on the species of molecules in the gas, because that is already taken care of by choosing a gram-molecule as the unit of amount in n. Hence K can depend only on the temperature.

By what law does K depend on the temperature? Surely it increases with the temperature, since the volume of a gas increases with increasing temperature at a constant pressure. Of course, K would increase with the temperature in an especially simple way if it were directly proportional to the temperature. But is it?

The Absolute Temperature Scale

In order to answer that question, you must recall how we usually measure a temperature. We measure it by a "thermometer" —a glass tube connected to a bulb filled with mercury or alcohol. Before we use the thermometer, it is put in ice water, a mark is made at the level of the mercury, and a number is engraved beside that mark—zero for a centigrade thermometer, 32 for a Fahrenheit thermometer. Then the thermometer is put in boiling water and another mark is made, beside which 100 is en-

■ DEFINING ABSOLUTE TEMPERATURE ■

The absolute temperature scale can be defined by taking the K in Boyle's Law as being proportional to that temperature, or $K = RT$. Then, writing the resulting expression for two volumes at two temperatures and the same pressure, $pV_1 = nRT_1$ and $pV_2 = nRT_2$, we can subtract one from the other to get

$$p(V_1 - V_2) = nR(T_1 - T_2).$$

This means that the change in volume of a gas, when it is heated at constant pressure, is proportional to the change in temperature. Thus this definition of temperature is consistent with the experimental result announced in 1802 by Gay-Lussac: "All gases, whatever be their density . . . expand equally between the same degrees of heat." The constant, R, is usually chosen so that temperature differences on the absolute scale are the same as temperature differences on the centigrade scale. The absolute zero is then at −273 degrees centigrade.

---

graved on a centigrade thermometer and 212 on a Fahrenheit thermometer. The distance between those marks is then divided in equal parts — 100 parts on a centigrade thermometer and 180 parts on a Fahrenheit thermometer.

Clearly these numbers were really pulled out of a hat — the hats of Anders Celsius and Gabriel Fahrenheit. We might just as well choose some other temperature as zero, or divide the scale into finer or coarser units. In particular, we might choose K, the constant of proportionality in the gas law, for "the temperature."

That is almost exactly what is done to make the scale of *absolute temperatures*. For that scale the temperature is taken as proportional to K, rather than as K itself. It is taken as proportional, not identical, in order to have such numbers for the temperature that a difference in temperature of "one degree" will be the same on the absolute scale and the centigrade scale. In other words, K is made equal to RT, where T denotes the absolute temperature, and R is a constant of proportionality chosen in the way described in "Defining Absolute Temperature" (above).

The constant R, often called the *gas constant*, has an unusual and interesting property. It is independent of what gas you are dealing with, and of the circumstances in which you deal with it. In other words, it is a "universal constant." In Chapter 3 you have already met another such constant of nature — Planck's constant, h.

This simple law, $pV = nRT$, is not exactly obeyed by any gas

■   PRESSURE AND MOLECULAR SPEED   ■

Bernouilli suggested that the pressure in a gas held at constant volume is proportional to the square of the speed, v, of its particles. More detailed examination shows that his suggestion can be written in the form

$$pV = \frac{1}{3}nN_0mv^2,$$

where n is the number of gram-molecules of the gas, N_0 is the number of molecules in each gram-molecule (Avogadro's number), and m is the mass of each molecule. Comparing this with the perfect gas law, $pV = nRT$, shows that the temperature is proportional to the square of the speed of the particles:

$$RT = \frac{1}{3}N_0mv^2;$$

in other words, proportional to the total kinetic energy of the particles.

---

over the entire range of temperatures and pressures. Deviations of the behavior of the gas from the law become evident at high pressures and at low temperatures — the conditions in which the molecules of the gas become more densely packed together. Then the sizes of the molecules, and the attractions between them, begin to have noteworthy effects. But the law is obeyed very well by "perfect gases" — gases that are dilute enough so that the sizes of their molecules make up only a negligible part of their total volume.

Temperature and Molecular Speed

Turn now to examine the second part of Bernouilli's insight — that the pressure of a gas held at constant volume should be proportional to the square of the velocity of the "aerial particles." Remember that the kinetic energy of a moving particle is equal to $1/2\ mv^2$, where m is its mass and v is its velocity. Bernouilli's proposal would make the pressure, of any particular gas, at any particular volume, proportional to the kinetic energy of the particles.

But according to the perfect gas law, the pressure of *any* gas, at *any* volume, is also proportional to its absolute temperature. It is tempting to guess, therefore, that the absolute temperature is proportional to the kinetic energy of the particles, at all volumes. By following up this guess in detail, you would find it justified; the result is shown in "Pressure and Molecular Speed" (above).

■ CONDUCTIVITY OF A METAL ■

The mean free path, l, of the mobile electrons between effective collisions is given by the relation

$$l = vt; \qquad t = \frac{l}{v}$$

between the mean free path, the mean free time, and the speed. The speed can be expressed in terms of the absolute temperature by using the equation derived before:

$$v = \sqrt{\frac{3RT}{N_0 m}}.$$

Then, using this expression for v, and substituting the resulting value of t in the expression for the conductivity, σ, derived in Chapter 5,

$$\sigma = \frac{Ne^2 t}{2m},$$

we can express the conductivity in terms of the mean free path and the absolute temperature:

$$\sigma = \frac{Ne^2 l}{2} \sqrt{\frac{N_0}{3mRT}}.$$

The Mean Free Path

This is the algebraic apparatus that Drude used to make a theory of the mean free time of the electrons in a metal. He reasoned that the speeds of the electrons, rushing about randomly at ordinary temperatures, would be very large compared with any drift velocity that an applied electric force would give to those electrons. Then he could replace the "mean free time" by a "mean free path"—the average distance traveled by an electron between its effective collisions with the ions in the metal—by multiplying the mean free time by the random speed. For the random speed he could use the relation that we have just discussed—the relation between that speed and the absolute temperature. "Conductivity of a Metal" (above) shows the algebraic steps in this procedure.

After the construction of a theory that sounds reasonable, there comes the exciting moment when numbers are put into it and the calculated results are compared with the results of actual experiments. Drude's theory says, for example, that the conductivity of a metal should vary inversely with the square root of the temperature. What does the conductivity of a real metal really do?

Comparison of Theory with Experiment

In actual fact, the resistivities of metals do increase with increasing temperature, and their conductivities therefore decrease. But over a wide range of temperatures the conductivities vary inversely with the temperature itself, not with its square root. This suggests looking at other terms in Drude's formula, to see whether one of them might vary with the temperature in a way that would patch up this result.

What about N, the density of mobile electrons in the metal? If that number varied inversely with the square root of the temperature, the formula might become valid. But there is no reason to believe that the number of mobile electrons would decrease with increasing temperature. If that number varied at all, it should increase: The increasing heat-agitation of the ions might shake loose additional electrons, but it could hardly immobilize electrons that are mobile at lower temperatures.

What about l, the mean free path of the mobile electrons? If the electrons are very tiny particles, then it seems improbable that their mean free path would decrease with increasing temperature. As the metal is heated, it expands and the obstacles to the traveling electrons get further apart: The electrons should find a longer, not a shorter, mean free path.

Indeed the mean free path behaves oddly in a number of ways. Putting measured conductivities into Drude's formula, you can calculate the mean free paths that the theory demands. They turn out to be several hundred times the distance between adjacent ions in the metal. It is hard to see how an electron could travel past so many densely packed ions before having an effective collision with one of them.

This last puzzle seems even harder to solve when you look at the effect of squeezing the metal by a high pressure. Compressing a metal surely pushes the ions closer together in it. But the conductivity of most metals *increases* with increasing pressure, as if the ions afforded an even longer mean free path to the electrons.

In view of these large faults in Drude's theory, you may ask why anybody pays attention to it. The answer is that, along with its failures, it achieves one remarkable success. Fifty years before Drude's time, it had been noticed that the ratio of the electrical conductivity to the heat conductivity of all metals is about the same when those data are obtained at the same temperature.

This observation, known as the Law of Wiedemann and Franz, had seemed inexplicable.

Recognizing that metals have very much higher heat conductivities than do insulators, Drude guessed that in metals heat, as well as electricity, is mostly conducted by the mobile electrons. He used his theory, therefore, to calculate the heat conductivity of the electron gas. The ratio of the two calculated conductivities turned out to correspond closely with the observed ratio.

Wien's Guesses

Such a success cannot be wholly ignored. In 1905 Hendrick Lorentz refined Drude's theory. But using the best theoretical methods of his day, he could not uncover the source of its fail-

LORENTZ

HENDRIK ANTOON LORENTZ (1853-1928) *spent most of his life in the Netherlands city of Leyden, where he was first a student and later became professor of mathematical physics. From the outset his principal interest was in the explanation of electromagnetic phenomena in matter and in empty space.*

Lorentz's early work was devoted mostly to providing a theoretical picture, rigorously derived, of the electromagnetic behavior of matter. In this effort he pioneered in the application of James Clerk Maxwell's electromagnetic theory to a medium composed of discrete molecules, attempting to give a satisfying explanation of the reflection and refraction of light by both insulating and conducting materials, and the quantitative variation of these properties with the wavelength of the light. When the electron was identified in 1897, he immediately set out to apply the electromagnetic theory to the behavior of electrons in solids, and in 1909 published his best-known book, "The Theory of Electrons."

Lorentz's parallel concern with the theory of electromagnetic fields in empty space made him an important forerunner of Albert Einstein. Thus in 1895 he introduced the idea of "local time," and eight years later he arrived at the "Lorentz transformation" which forms the basis for the special theory of relativity. His broad interest led him to contribute also to thermodynamics, the kinetic theory of matter, and the theories of gravitation and of radiation. He provided the theoretical background for the experimental observations of his compatriot, Pieter Zeeman, on the effects of a magnetic field on the wavelengths of light in the spectra of the elements, and the two men jointly received the Nobel Prize for physics in 1902, in recognition of that work.

ures. At last in 1913 Wilhelm Wien made two bold guesses, with little more justification than that they would salvage Drude's theory.

Wien's first guess was that, for some reason, the average speed of the electrons in the electron gas does not obey the laws established for ordinary gases. In particular he suggested that the average speed is not proportional to the square root of the absolute temperature,

$$v = \sqrt{\frac{3RT}{N_0 m}},$$

WILHELM WIEN (1864-1928), *after studying in Göttingen, Heidelberg and Berlin,
entered the Physico-Technical Institute at
Charlottenburg as assistant to Helmholtz.
He went on to hold professorships in several German universities, and finally in
Munich, meanwhile conducting both theoretical and experimental researches into a
wide variety of physical problems.*

*Wien is best known for his work on
"black-body radiation," rewarded by the
Nobel Prize for physics in 1911. He devel-*

WILHELM WIEN

*oped a formula describing how the radi-
ated energy is distributed among the various wavelengths in the radiation. One consequence of the formula is "Wien's displacement law,"
stating that the wavelength which carries the maximum energy is inversely proportional to the absolute temperature of the radiator. This
work provided important links in the chain that led Planck to invent the
quantum theory of radiation in 1900.*

*Wien wrote also on other optical problems, on water currents and air
currents, and on X-rays, cathode rays, and electrical discharge through
gases at low pressure. Especially noteworthy is his pioneering work on
rays of positively charged particles, which he identified as early as
1898 by deflecting them with both electric and magnetic forces.*

*Wien's suggestions for salvaging Drude's theory of electronic con-
duction in metals form an interesting instance of an insight that could
only receive justification by much later and broader theoretical work.
Others made alternative suggestions that have fallen out of notice. In
particular F. A. Lindemann (later Lord Cherwell) elaborated a theory in
which the free electrons form a space-lattice, interleaved with the
space-lattice of the crystalline ions of the metal, held in considerable
rigidity by the large electrostatic forces within the metal, and moving
bodily under electrical forces applied from outside. His theory had
much to commend it so long as it was possible to regard the electrons
as tiny particles, each rigorously localized in space; but it cannot
stand close scrutiny today when each electron is pictured as a wave-
packet extending over many atoms.*

but is completely independent of the temperature. In Drude's formula for the conductivity,

$$\sigma = \frac{Ne^2l}{2} \sqrt{\frac{N_0}{3mRT}},$$

the variation of the conductivity with the temperature comes entirely from the variation with temperature in the average speed of the mobile electrons. Hence, if only the first of Wien's guesses were adopted, Drude's formula would yield a conductivity in metals that is entirely independent of the temperature – a result worse than before.

But the second of Wien's guesses restored and corrected the temperature dependence. He put emphasis on the fact that the ions in a metal are not at rest but are engaging in heat-vibrations, whose amplitude increases as the temperature increases. And he suggested that the probability is greater that an electron will make an effective collision with an ion if the amplitude of vibration of the ion is larger.

Now it takes energy to make any particle vibrate, and the vibrational energy of the ions in a metal at any temperature accounts for the heat content of the metal at that temperature. It had long been known that the heat content of a metal, at ordinary temperatures, increases in direct proportion to its temperature. Accordingly, Wien made his suggestion quantitative: The probability of an effective collision by a mobile electron with an ion in a metal increases in direct proportion to the heat content of the metal. Thus Wien's second guess makes the mean free path of the mobile electrons inversely proportional to the absolute temperature, and gives the right temperature dependence to the conductivity in Drude's formula.

Notice an interesting effect of Wien's guesses on the picture of conduction by the electron gas in a metal. They shift the responsibility, for the change of conductivity with temperature, entirely off of the electron gas, where Drude had put it, and place that responsibility on the ions, which Drude had ignored. Thirteen years later, wave mechanics provided a solid theoretical basis for Wien's guesses. It is pleasant to realize that Wien lived to see his insights justified.

7 Semiconductors

Admire again the indefatigable work, the careful observation of Michael Faraday! As part of his examination of electrical conduction by whatever he could lay hands on, he passed an electric current through solid silver sulfide in 1833. He noticed that its conductivity increased when he raised its temperature.

Now, the little trickle of current that an ionic crystal will conduct behaves in the same way: As the temperature increases, the trickle increases. In this kind of materials the charge carriers for the current are the ions that compose the crystal. Assisted by the presence of vacancies in the crystalline arrangement, a few ions can move through the crystal in the way that Chapter 5 described. As the temperature increases, the more vigorous vibration of the ions permits them to squeeze into the vacancies more readily. Hence the conductivity of the crystal increases with rising temperature.

This behavior is the reverse of the behavior of metals; the conductivity of metals *decreases* with increasing temperature. The charge carriers in metals are mobile electrons, not the ions that the electrons have left behind them. But the activities of those ions are responsible nevertheless for the decrease in conductivity with increasing temperature. By making those ions vibrate more vigorously, the increasing temperature increases the frequency with which the mobile electrons are scattered from their paths. Thus, as Chapter 6 described, the electrons suffer more frequent losses of the added velocity that an electrical force tries to give to them.

Since silver sulfide behaves in this respect more like an ionic crystal than like a metal, it is tempting to ascribe its conduction of electricity to the motion of ions. But it conducts suspiciously well — not as well as a metal, to be sure, but much better than an ionic crystal. Moreover the products of ionic conduction that appear at the electrodes are not sufficient to account for all the charge that is transported. Faraday had shown, by the studies of electrolysis described in Chapter 2, that there is a strict relation between the *charge* transported and the *material* transported when the charge carriers are ions.

Some Properties of Semiconductors

As the years passed, a few more such *semiconductors* were discovered, and many curious properties were observed in them. These properties were exploited in technological applications, and arts of fabrication were perfected to make them more useful, even though there remained little physical understanding of their behavior. For example, in 1873 it was discovered that the electrical resistance of the semiconductor selenium could be reduced by shining light on it. In the following year several investigators found instances in which a contact between a metal and a semiconductor shows a resistance that does not obey Ohm's Law: The resistance varies both with the magnitude and with the direction of the applied voltage.

This *nonohmic* phenomenon was exploited especially vigorously. Devices made of copper oxide or of selenium were perfected for use as rectifiers of alternating current. The development of radio communication created a demand for suitable radio detectors, and semiconductor rectifiers filling this need appeared in 1904; they were made by putting pointed wires in contact with a piece of galena, carborundum, tellurium, or silicon.

These "cat's whisker" detectors were soon displaced for most purposes by vacuum tubes. But, as radio communication began to exploit higher and higher frequencies, the frequency limitations of vacuum tubes became apparent. George Southworth, one of the men working in the forefront of high-frequency radio development, even visited second-hand radio markets in the 1930's to ferret out old, almost-obsolete silicon detectors to use at frequencies where vacuum tubes were not usable. The use of especially high frequency radio waves in radar during World War II stimulated intensive work on detectors made of silicon, at the hands of many people, in several well-equipped laboratories.

Postwar Semiconductor Research

After the war some of these people, retaining their war-born interest in semiconductors, turned to a more searching study of the physical principles underlying them. Fortunately there lay ready for them a comprehensive theory of semiconductors that had been constructed by Sir Alan Wilson in 1931 and 1932.

■ CHARGE-CARRIER MOBILITY ■

The mobility of a charge-carrier is a useful quantity to use in analyzing conductivities. As we saw in Chapter 5, the current density, j, in any conductor is the product of the number of charge carriers per unit volume, N, times the charge on each carrier, $-e$, times the average drift velocity, V_D, or:

$$j = -NeV_D.$$

Dividing this equation by the electric force per unit charge, E, we get

$$\frac{j}{E} = -Ne\frac{V_D}{E},$$

in which the left side represents the conductivity, which we represent as σ, and the right side suggests defining a *mobility* — the drift velocity per unit force — which we designate by μ:

$$\mu = \frac{-V_D}{E}.$$

Then the conductivity is the product of the mobile charge density, Ne, and its mobility:

$$\sigma = Ne\mu.$$

Couched in wave-mechanical terms, it gave a clear picture of the electronic behavior to be expected in both pure and impure semiconductors. This theory has been amply verified by experiment in more recent years.

But clearly an experimental study of semiconductors was not easy to do. For example, there had been uncertainty, whether the nonohmic behavior of a contact between a metal and a semiconductor was a property of the semiconductor alone — a "volume property" — or of the contact between it and the metal — a "surface property." But how could anybody examine experimentally the electrical properties of a semiconductor without making contact with it? Nevertheless, a diversity of experiments had made it clear by 1935 that the nonohmic property belongs to the contact, not to the insides of the semiconducting material.

When research on such questions reappeared after the war, it was aimed at an understanding of silicon and its close ally, germanium. The choice was dictated by a principle that is almost always useful in scientific investigation: Simplify the problem as much as possible. Silicon and germanium are single chemical elements, falling successively below carbon in Group IV of the Periodic Table (Table II). And they crystallize with a simple atomic arrangement, well understood, in which the atoms are tied together by pure covalent bonds of the type described in Chapter 4. In fact, the arrangement of atoms in their crystals is the same as that of the carbon atoms in a diamond, pictured in Figure 17.

Research on these two materials over the past twenty years has constructed, on the base laid earlier by Wilson, most of our present picture of semiconductors, to be described in this chapter, and of the junctions between them, to be described in the next chapter. Silicon and germanium are indeed prototypes — "ideal" semiconductors. Their conductivities are intermediate between those of ionic crystals and those of metals. Like ionic crystals, and unlike metals, their conductivities increase with increasing temperature. But no electrolytic products form on the electrodes when a current passes through them. In other words, there is no evidence that ions carry the electrical current through these semiconductors; their conductivity is electronic, like that of metals.

Conductivity of Semiconductors

The first problem to settle is why the conductivity of semiconductors is so much less than that of metals, when both conductivities are electronic. Our earlier analysis, in Figure 26, makes clear that there are two places to look for this difference: Either the density of *charge carriers, N,* is less in semiconductors, or their drift velocity, V_D, is less under the same electric force.

In discussing metals in Chapter 5 we made theories about the drift velocity, which related that quantity to a mean free time, or a mean free path, for the mobile electrons. The conspicuous differences between semiconductors and metals now counsel caution in taking over such ideas uncritically. But surely drift velocity remains a suitable idea: the charge carriers must exhibit some average drift velocity in order to conduct an electric current.

Of course the drift velocity of the carriers increases with the electric force applied to them. It would be pleasant to be able to use *some* quantity that, like the mean free time or the mean free path, is a property of the material independent of the applied electric force. The quantity commonly used in speaking of semiconductors is the *average drift velocity per unit force,* called the *mobility* of the charge carriers. Then, as "Charge-Carrier Mobility" on page 94 shows, the conductivity is the

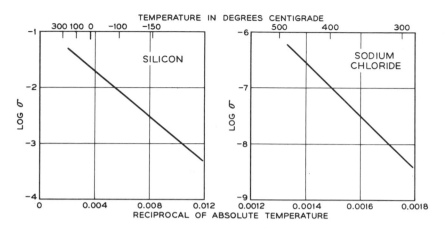

FIGURE 29 – PLOTS OF CONDUCTIVITY *versus temperature show that the vari-*
ations of conductivity with temperature have the same form for a semiconductor
(left) and an ionic crystal (right). The form is a straight line when the logarithm
of the conductivity is plotted against the reciprocal of the absolute temperature.
This is the form that theories predict for almost any process in which heat energy
excites some of a large collection of molecules to perform that process.

product of the mobility and the density of the mobile charges.

It is not easy to find an experiment that will separate these two factors and so assign to one of them the responsibility for the relatively low conductivities of semiconductors. But a strong clue to the answer comes from the shape of the curve showing how a semiconductor's conductivity varies with temperature. As Figure 29 demonstrates, that shape closely resembles the shape of the same curve for an ionic crystal: The magnitudes of the conductivities are very different, but the way they vary with the temperature is the same.

Now in an ionic crystal the increase in conductivity with increasing temperature can be explained by the fact that an increasing number of ions acquire enough energy to surmount the energy barrier that impedes them from squeezing into a vacancy. This suggests that, in the case of semiconductors, increasing the temperature may give more electrons enough energy to escape from bound states and become free to wander.

Would you call that an increase in the number of carriers or an increase in their mobility? It is customary to call it an increase in their number. In any conduction process, one counts only the charge carriers that are free to wander; and if their freedom is only momentary, one counts those that are free at the moment.

If you accept the idea that the conductivity of a semiconductor is relatively low because a relatively small number of electrons are free to wander at any one moment, you can determine what that number is. In pure silicon at room temperature, there is only one charge carrier for every million million atoms.

Freeing Electrons by Heat

How are these few charge carriers made free? You can make a good guess by looking at the diagram of *first ionization potentials* for the elements in Figure 22. The points for silicon and germanium in that diagram are located just above the dividing line below which the atomic species always form metals. Clearly the heat energy contributes just the little bit of energy necessary to set some of the electrons free.

What are those electrons doing when they are *not* free? You can guess the answer from our study of covalent bonds in Chapter 4. That earlier discussion pointed out that each carbon atom in a diamond has four nearest-neighbor atoms, and each atom shares its four outermost electrons with those neighbors, to form *electron-pair bonds*. Since the first ionization potential of a carbon atom is fairly high, heat energy is insufficient to free the electrons from those bonds at ordinary temperatures. In silicon and germanium the atoms adopt the same arrangement as the carbon atoms in a diamond; but now heat energy can occasionally eject an electron from an electron-pair bond. Figure 30 pictures this ejection in a schematic way.

But why only "occasionally?" If the heat energy is adequate to eject an electron from a bond, why does it not eject an electron from *every* bond? The answer comes from the nature of heat. Calculating the total heat energy in a piece of silicon, and dividing that total by the number of atoms in the piece, you would find that the average heat energy per atom is a very small fraction of the energy required to eject one electron. But heat is a bumbling business. As the silicon atoms vibrate about their positions in the crystal, one atom or another occasionally sustains a hard enough kick to acquire much more energy than the average. It will usually lose that energy almost at once by kicking its neighbors. But it may instead, during its brief period of especially energetic vibration, kick an electron out of one of its four bonds.

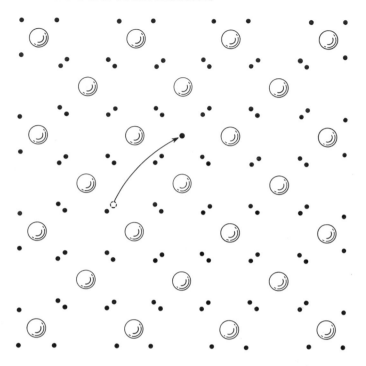

FIGURE 30 – EJECTING AN ELECTRON *from an electron-pair bond in a semi-conductor frees it to act as a charge carrier for conduction of electricity.*

Freed Electrons and Holes

The electrons thus freed dash about in the semiconductor somewhat as do the free electrons in a metal. Such a freed electron stays free so long as it is moving in a neighborhood where all the electron-pair bonds have their full complement of electrons. When an electromotive force is applied to the semiconductor, the freed electrons acquire a drift velocity in the direction of the force.

But any of these electrons stands some chance of drifting into a place where there is another bond that has lost an electron. Then it may settle into that bond, remaking the bond into an electron-pair bond and losing the extra bit of energy that it acquired earlier. In other words, any one electron is not permanently freed by its extra bit of energy. It has an average "lifetime" as a freed electron. In counting the number of charge carriers in a semiconductor, you can count any one of the electrons only while it is free.

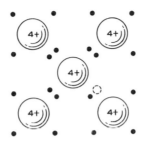

FIGURE 31 – THE NEIGHBORHOOD *of a bond that has lost one electron acquires a net positive charge, equal and opposite to the charge on the ejected electron. The resulting unbalance of charge is called a* hole.

Look now at the bond that a freed electron leaves behind it. The bond is bereft of one of the two electrons that make up its normal bonding complement. Since that part of the solid was electrically neutral before the electron escaped, the neighborhood of the bond is left with a net positive charge when the negatively charged electron departs (Figure 31).

This positively charged region, which has been newly formed, then acquires a life of its own. An electron can move into it from a neighboring bond, as Figure 32 suggests, restoring the pairing of electrons in it but leaving behind an entirely similar bond newly bereft of one electron. As the process of electron replacing electron continues, the positively charged region moves always in the opposite direction from the electrons, to the region last deserted by an electron.

This motion is very much like the replacement of ion by ion when a vacancy is present in an ionic crystal described in Chapter 5. Again, as in Figure 24, it is helpful to imagine a fictitious "particle." Instead of thinking of a succession of small electronic motions, it is convenient to think of the process as if the positively charged region were a positively charged "particle," dashing in a random way through the solid much as a freed electron dashes. Under an electromotive force, the replacement of a bonding vacancy by an electron is slightly more likely to take place from the direction favored by the force. In other words, the positively charged "particle" acquires a drift velocity and becomes a charge carrier, usually called a *hole*.

Hence, when an electron is freed from its bonding duties, *two* charge carriers arise, of equal and opposite electric charge. Under an electromotive force, both carriers acquire drift veloci-

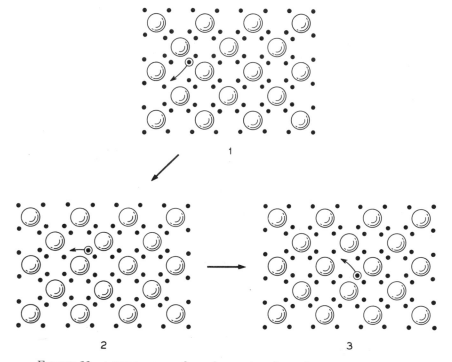

FIGURE 32 – A HOLE MOVES *through a semiconductor by acquiring an electron from a neighboring bond. In successive steps, the hole can move throughout the crystal.*

ties, in opposite directions. Since opposite charges drifting in opposite directions represent electric currents in the same direction, the currents produced by freed electrons and by holes are additive.

Recombination of Electrons and Holes

When an electron encounters a hole, the two may *recombine,* and then both charge carriers disappear. From the way in which these carriers arise, it is clear that both sorts must have the same lifetime. But there is no reason to expect that they will have the same mobility. Indeed, you might expect that the mobility of the holes would be much less than that of the freed electrons because of the complicated stepwise process by which they move. It turns out, however, that the mobility of holes is usually only slightly less than that of freed electrons.

Notice that, unlike the free electrons in a metal, the freed electrons in a semiconductor change their identities from moment to moment. The electrons that are drifting at one moment may all have recombined with holes at a later moment, to be replaced by other electrons newly freed by the heat vibrations of the solid. The processes of ejection from bonds and recombination in bonds are going on constantly. The fact that the conductivity is the same from moment to moment reflects the fact that ejections and recombinations are proceeding at the same rate. Figure 33 schematizes the charge carriers that might be found in a semiconductor at some one moment.

The Law of Mass Action

By thinking closely about the balance between the rates of ejection and recombination, you can easily derive an important rule governing the concentrations of holes and freed electrons in a semiconductor. In the first place, since ejection and recombination must be proceeding at the same rate, then, if we calculate the rate of either process alone, we have automatically calculated the rate of the other process also.

The recombination process is the easier to talk about; the argument goes like this. What is the chance that a *particular* freed electron will encounter a hole in some fixed length of time? Whatever that chance may be, it is surely directly proportional to the number of holes per cubic centimeter that are moving about and waiting to meet electrons. What is the total number of freed electrons that will encounter holes in that same length of time? Surely that number will be proportional to the chance that any one of them does, multiplied by the number of freed electrons per cubic centimeter that are in search of holes.

Thus the rate at which holes and freed electrons disappear must be proportional to the product of the density of freed

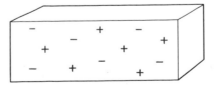

FIGURE 33 – A SEMICONDUCTOR *can be visualized as a medium in which there are dilute concentrations of positively charged holes and negatively charged electrons, all free to wander.*

electrons times the density of holes. And those densities must be maintained by the reverse process, in which freed electrons and holes are regenerated by heat vibrations at the same rate. Hence you can conclude that the product of the two densities must stay constant with time.

The resulting rule is usually written $np = K$, where n is the density of freed electrons (*negative* carriers) and p is the density of holes (*positive* carriers). Since these densities increase with increasing temperature, the constant, K, must vary with the temperature. But that constant does *not* vary with changes of n and p at any one temperature. This fact is very important in deciding what will happen when there are impurities in the semiconductor.

Impurity Semiconductors

It turns out that almost any impurity increases the conductivity of a semiconductor. Impurities invariably *decrease* the conductivities of metals, by reducing the mobilities of the free electrons in them. It is reasonable to guess that in semiconductors the impurities will not reverse their role and increase the mobility of the freed electrons. Impurities must therefore affect the conductivity of a semiconductor by increasing the density of the charge carriers in it.

In silicon and germanium it is especially easy to see how certain kinds of impurities might contribute additional charge carriers. The atomic species that affect the conductivity in the

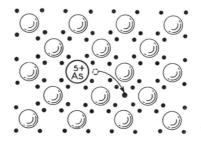

FIGURE 34 – AN ARSENIC ATOM *can be substituted for a germanium atom in a crystal of germanium. It donates an extra electron that is free to wander, but no compensating hole. The compensating positive electric charge is frozen in place on the arsenic ion. Any such impurity is called a* donor.

most drastic and systematic way are those which fall in the third and fifth columns of the Periodic Table—the columns immediately to the right and left of the fourth column in which silicon and germanium are found.

For example, the addition of as little as one millionth of one per cent of arsenic to pure germanium doubles its conductivity at room temperature. In the technological uses of semiconductors, effects such as that are of utmost importance. Much attention has been devoted to developing means for making extraordinarily pure silicon and germanium, and for adding extremely small and well controlled amounts of impurities.

Arsenic in Germanium

Since arsenic falls immediately to the right of germanium in the Periodic Table, you know that an atom of arsenic must have one more electron than an atom of germanium, and that its positive nuclear charge must be one unit greater. Entering the solid, the arsenic atom looks almost like a germanium atom, and adopts a position in which it sees four next-neighboring germanium atoms. However, since the arsenic has one more electron in an outer orbit than the bonding with four neighbors will absorb, it contributes an extra electron, which has no bonding role and which finds itself very loosely bound to its environment. This electron is indistinguishable from those that we have already talked about—those that have been freed from bonds by the heat vibrations. It can drift like its fellow in an electromotive force and contribute to the conductivity.

Notice, however, one important new feature of the impure crystal. The compensating positive charge for the thermally freed electron is provided by a hole, which is free to wander itself. The corresponding compensating charge for the electron introduced by the arsenic atom is provided by the additional unit of charge on the nucleus of the atom, and that is frozen in place. In other words, the wandering *impurity electron* leaves a fixed, positively charged, arsenic ion behind it; the electron contributes only itself as a charge carrier, *without* a corresponding hole, as Figure 34 suggests. In this way a small amount of arsenic upsets the balance of freed electrons and holes: There will be more freed electrons than holes in the impure germanium.

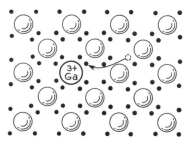

FIGURE 35 – A GALLIUM ATOM, *substituted for a germanium atom in crystalline germanium, contributes an extra hole by accepting an electron from a neighboring bond and thus freezing a negative charge on the gallium ion, which compensates the positive charge on the mobile hole. Such an impurity is called an acceptor.*

Gallium in Germanium

The balance can also be upset in the converse way by introducing, as impurities, atomic species falling in the third column of the Periodic Table. For example, if an atom of gallium is added as an impurity, it will adopt the position that an atom of germanium usually occupies. But, since gallium has one *less* electron than the germanium atom, it will lack one electron for completing four bonds. The bond thus skimped constitutes a hole into which an electron from a neighboring bond can move, and thus the hole can wander in just the way that thermally generated holes do. Now, however, the gallium atom has acquired one more electron than the positive charge on its nucleus can compensate; the wandering hole leaves behind it a negative gallium ion frozen in place, as Figure 35 schematizes.

Calculating the Charge-Carrier Total

How many charge carriers altogether does the semiconductor have when such impurities have been added? Holes and freed electrons are still being generated by the heat vibrations. Do the impurities simply add the total number of carriers that they have contributed? No, the rule that the product of n and p is constant still applies: If you retrace the reasoning by which you derived the rule, you will see that it made no assumptions about how the electrons and holes came to be in the semiconductor. Hence, for example, by contributing extra holes, the gallium atoms must reduce the number of freed electrons.

In order to calculate how many charge carriers the impure semiconductor contains, you can think in the following way. The total number of carriers is *n plus p*. The rule just derived says that *n times p* must be the same as it is when there are no impurities. You need one more relation between *n* and *p*—then you can calculate what *n* and *p* are separately and add them.

You can arrive at that additional relation if you remember how these carriers arose. The thermally generated carriers come in pairs: There are the same numbers of freed electrons and holes introduced thermally. And for each freed electron or hole introduced by an impurity, there is a compensating ion of opposite charge frozen in the material. In other words, the whole bit of solid stays electrically neutral.

Then the total number of positive charges equals the total number of negative charges. You can write $N_- + n = N_+ + p$, where N_- is the number of (negative) gallium ions, and N_+ is the number of (positive) arsenic ions. And you can take the numbers of ions as being equal to the numbers of impurity atoms that you put into the semiconductor, on the assumption that those atoms were all ionized.

If you play with these two simple equations—one providing the difference and the other the product of *n* and *p*—you can assure yourself of several things. In the first place, by adding one type of impurity you will always increase the density of one type of carrier, reduce the density of the other, and increase the total density of carriers. In the second place, by adding both types of impurities you can make the semiconductor look as if it were pure, so far as the number of charge carriers can show you. But the impurities will reduce the conductivity somewhat, by reducing the *mobility* of the charge carriers.

Some Semiconductor Terminology

There are some helpful words that are commonly used in talking about *impurity* semiconductors. The addition of impurities is called *doping*. Impurities like arsenic are called *donors* because they donate freed electrons; impurities like gallium are called *acceptors* because they accept an electron from neighboring bonds. Charge carriers of the more numerous type are called the *majority carriers*, and the others the *minority carriers*. A semiconductor is called *p-type* or *n-type* according to whether holes or freed electrons are the majority carriers.

Almost all the devices employing semiconductors that have come into use in electrical technology embody *junctions* at which semiconductors of these two types are in intimate contact. The next chapter will describe the principles that govern the behavior of some of those devices — the rectifier, the solar cell, and the transistor.

8 P-N Junctions

Studying the physics of a single material in a penetrating way is not easy. We have been trying to do it in the last three chapters. Studying the physics of two materials stuck together is more than twice as hard; we will do it now. It is more than twice as hard because we must know the physics of both the materials that are stuck together, and in addition the physics of what happens where they join.

You will say that even a "single material" is stuck to something — to the air or even just to a vacuum — and you are right. But we have not been studying that fact. If we had studied thermionic emission or photoemission — how metals may eject electrons into the air or the vacuum when they are strongly heated or illuminated — we would have encountered difficulties similar to those that we might encounter now.

Part of the difficulty of studying junctions, boundaries, surfaces, comes from the fact that there is so little of them. A one-inch cube of a solid contains about a million million million million atoms, and only about one ten-millionth of them are set at the surface. Certainly those atoms are in a very special place; for example, the forces on them from outside the cube bear no resemblance to the forces from inside the cube. Hence the surface atoms might behave quite differently from the way the atoms buried in the cube behave. But there are too few of these atoms for us to find out much about them. Physicists and chemists have broken their heads and their hearts in a century of research on surfaces.

Semiconductor Junctions

Fortunately, however, the junctions that we will study in this chapter offer a minimum of these difficulties. They are formed between two pieces of a single material — germanium or silicon — and in all ordinary ways those pieces scarcely differ. One piece

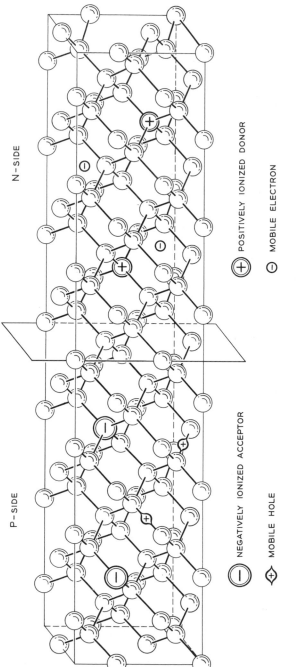

N-SIDE

P-SIDE

⊖ NEGATIVELY IONIZED ACCEPTOR

⬦ MOBILE HOLE

⊕ POSITIVELY IONIZED DONOR

⊖ MOBILE ELECTRON

FIGURE 36 – A P-N JUNCTION is formed by incorporating substitutional impurities (Figures 34 and 35) into a single crystal of silicon or germanium. Each acceptor impurity atom on the p-side of the junction, chosen from the elements in Group III of the Periodic Table, becomes a negative ion by accepting an electron from one of the covalent bonds between the germanium or silicon atoms and leaving a mobile hole. Each donor impurity atom on the n-side of the junction, chosen from the elements in Group V of the Periodic Table, becomes a positive ion by donating an electron that wanders freely through the structure. The donor and acceptor ions remain frozen in place and cannot wander.

contains a tiny amount of an impurity that acts as a *donor* as the last chapter described, and the other piece an equally tiny amount of an *acceptor*. The donor provides extra mobile electrons, making the first piece an n-type semiconductor. The acceptor, by introducing extra mobile holes, makes the second piece a p-type semiconductor. The place where one piece meets the other is called a *p-n junction*.

But to speak of "one piece meeting the other" may be deceptive. Their "meeting" is so intimate that these "pieces" together form a continuous solid. In fact at their best, p-n junctions are made in a single crystal of the semiconductor, of which one part is doped with acceptors and an adjoining part is doped with donors.

Since the concentrations of donors and acceptors are very small, the crystal continues to look like a single crystal, and in most ways to behave like one. As Figure 36 shows, there is no interruption of the regular crystalline arrangement of the atoms. The physical situation is roughly analogous to one in which a very dilute solution of salt has been carefully poured on top of a very dilute solution of sugar. The result is mostly water through and through, and only a keen sense of taste or a careful chemical analysis can find the difference between top and bottom.

Diffusion

It is helpful to push a little further the analogy between a p-n junction and the boundary between two dilute solutions. If you let the two solutions sit in a quiet place for awhile, one on top of the other, the boundary between them becomes less and less definite, because sugar diffuses toward the salty side and salt toward the sweet side. This diffusion occurs because the molecules of the sugar and the ions of the salt are moving about with heat-motions in a random way. The water restrains them somewhat, but the water does not fix for each molecule a neighborhood from which it can never stray. Ultimately any one of them might get anywhere at all in the water.

As a result of these diffusive motions, the molecules and ions all tend to mix with one another. And you will find that, on the average, molecules of both salt and sugar are moving from the region in which their concentration is higher to the region in which it is lower.

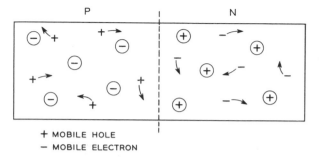

FIGURE 37 – IN A P-N JUNCTION *the ionized impurities (circled pluses and minuses) are fixed in place while the holes and mobile electrons wander.*

At first this analogy may seem irrelevant to a semiconductor, which is solid, not liquid. The impurity-ions are constrained to vibrate about fixed positions and cannot wander randomly. But the freed electrons and holes can wander, as Figure 37 illustrates. During their lifetimes, before recombination immobilizes and neutralizes them, the mobile electrons will tend to diffuse from places where they are numerous to places where they are sparse, and so also will the mobile holes.

Diffusion in a Semiconductor

The Russian theoretical physicist Yakov Frenkel was the first to emphasize the importance of diffusion in the flow of charge carriers through a semiconductor. He recognized especially clearly that, when the carriers are not uniformly distributed through the semiconductor, they will flow in the direction of lower concentration, even though no electrical force is applied to them.

This is the principal phenomenon that becomes newly important at a p-n junction in a semiconductor. Since holes are more

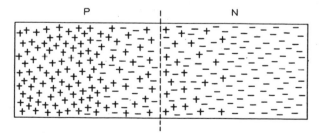

FIGURE 38 – DIFFUSION *will bring some of the mobile holes across a p-n junction into its n-side, and some of the mobile electrons into its p-side.*

numerous on the p-side of the junction, and freed electrons are more numerous on the n-side, each species tends to diffuse across the junction to the side where it is less numerous, in the way suggested in Figure 38. In other words, the charge carriers now drift not only when they are urged by an electric force but also when their concentration differs from place to place. By analyzing the consequences of these two causes of drift, you can understand the electrical properties of a p-n junction.

The first consequence is the appearance of net electric charges in the neighborhood of the junction. The holes diffusing across the junction carry their positive charges with them, and leave behind them the negatively charged acceptor ions. Similarly the mobile electrons, diffusing in the opposite direction, leave positively charged donor ions.

Thus, two important differences arise between the semiconducting material near the junction and the same material further away. In the first place, diffusion depletes the nearby material of its normal complement of charge carriers, as Figure 39 shows. In the second place, the nearby material is no longer electrically neutral: It exhibits a net positive charge on the n-side and

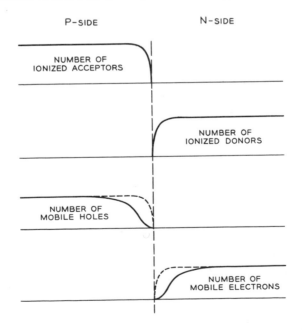

FIGURE 39 – DEPLETION *of majority charge carriers, at either side of a p-n junction, takes place because the carriers diffuse across the junction.*

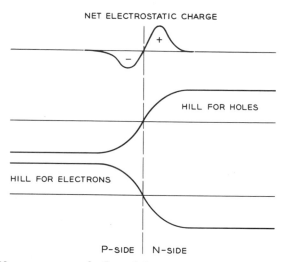

NET ELECTROSTATIC CHARGE

HILL FOR HOLES

HILL FOR ELECTRONS

P-SIDE | N-SIDE

FIGURE 40 – BARRIERS *to the flow of charge carriers at the junction are erected by the net electric charges that appear on either side of the junction. The opposition offered by those barriers can be pictured as a hill which the mobile charges must climb in order to leave the region from which they diffuse — a hill that faces in opposite directions for holes and for electrons.*

a net negative charge on the p-side, diagrammed at the top of Figure 40.

It may puzzle you that these changes occur only near the junction. If diffusion continues, why do the diffusing electrons and holes fail to equalize their numbers throughout the material? The answer is found in the limited lifetimes of a freed electron and a hole. In diffusing from a region in which they form a majority of the carriers to one in which they are in the minority, they find themselves in the country of their enemies. Before they can go far in that country, they are gobbled up by recombination with some of the great excess of their opposites.

Equilibrium at the Junction

From this description, you might conclude that, even when no electric force is applied from outside, there is a constant flow of holes across the junction from left to right, and of electrons from right to left. But in fact there is not, for a reason that is clear when you recall the effect of the charges possessed by the ionized impurities that contributed the charge carriers. The accumulation of ionic charge, of opposite sign to the mobile charge, tends to pull the mobile charge back. Hence, near the junction, another balance is accomplished: After diffusion has progressed enough to leave a fixed ionic charge, that charge not only opposes further diffusion but also attracts a compensatory flow in the *other* direction. Figure 40, therefore, represents a stationary condition near the junction – an equilibrium established by all these balances.

A good way to think about the balancing flows of charge carriers across the junction is to think of two equal and opposite currents of each species. Figure 41 pictures this way of thinking about the diffusing holes. The corresponding diagram for the mobile electrons would be similar, with the right and left sides interchanged.

In Figure 41, holes from the p-region, diffusing to the right across the junction, despite opposition by the charge on the positive ions, give an electric current I_f. Holes thermally generated

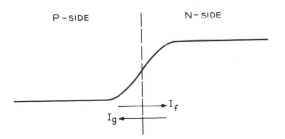

FIGURE 41 – AT EQUILIBRIUM *a current of holes,* I_f, *diffusing up the hill from the p-side where holes are the majority carriers, is balanced by an equal current,* I_g, *diffusing to the brow of the hill and sliding down from the n-side.*

in the n-region on the right are contributing an exactly compensating current I_g. You can imagine that the holes giving I_f are climbing up the "energy hill" in the diagram. The holes that give I_g wander randomly in the n-region until by chance they come to the brow of the hill and slide down.

Of course, in order to climb the hill and contribute to I_f, a hole must have enough energy to reach the top. Any less energetic holes attempting the ascent will slide back. The size of I_f will therefore depend on the height of the hill. How many holes can surmount it?

The answer to that question can be had by using statistical mechanics, a method of analysis that applies statistical thinking

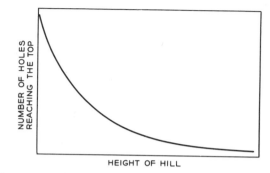

FIGURE 42 – THE NUMBER OF HOLES *able to climb the hill of Figure 41 increases greatly as the hill is lowered.*

to situations in which a very large number of particles – in this case, holes – are obeying general mechanical principles. Figure 42 shows the form of the result. The fraction of holes with enough energy to climb the hill increases rapidly as the height of the hill decreases, and consequently so does I_f.

But changing the height of the hill makes little change in I_g. That current depends on the rate at which holes are thermally generated in the n-region and survive their hostile environment long enough to diffuse to the brow of the hill. A hill of any height will urge ahead all holes that stray to its brow.

The Junction Rectifier

Picture now what happens when you disturb the balance across the junction by attaching the opposite poles of an electric battery to the opposite ends of the junction-bearing crystal. Urged by the electric force applied by the battery, holes and electrons acquire drift velocities, and these add to the velocities of their random motions. Since the holes bear a positive charge and the electrons a negative charge, their drift velocities are in opposite directions. But opposite charges moving in opposite directions give electric currents in the *same* direction. For that reason, we will only watch what happens to the holes, and be confident that the electric current contributed by the holes will be approximately doubled by the current due to the electrons.

But an even more important effect of connecting the electric battery to the semiconductor is that the height of the hill at the junction will be changed. If you connect the positive terminal of the battery to the n-side of the junction, and the negative terminal to the p-side, the battery assists the positive ions on the n-side to repel the holes; in other words, the battery increases the height of the hill, as shown in Figure 43(a). Reversing the battery connections lowers the hill, as you can see in Figure 43(b).

The resulting net current is plotted in Figure 44. It increases rapidly with the voltage of the battery, when the battery is connected so as to reduce the height of the hill. It increases less rapidly in the other direction, and finally becomes unchanging, when the battery raises the height of the hill. That final, unchanging *saturation current*, flowing when the hill is so high that almost no hole has enough energy to climb it—is just the current I_g in Figure 43.

Notice that the piece of germanium containing the p-n junction is far from obedient to Ohm's law. The rule that the current is proportional to the voltage, so useful for electrical conduction in metals, is inapplicable here: The junction offers a high re-

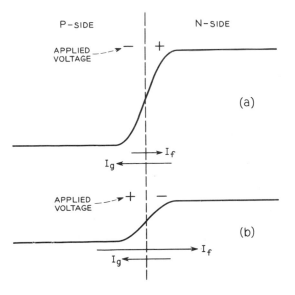

FIGURE 43 – THE HILL FOR HOLES *has a large effect on the current* (I_f) *of the holes that climb it, and a small effect on the current* (I_g) *of the holes that return. At equilibrium the two are equal and opposite (Figure 41). When the hill is raised (a) by applying a voltage in one direction,* I_f *is reduced, and the maximum current obtainable is* I_g*. When the hill is lowered (b) by reversing the sign of the voltage,* I_f *is greatly increased.*

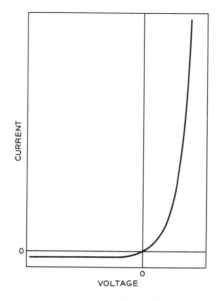

FIGURE 44 – THE ELECTRIC CURRENT *through a p-n junction increases greatly with increasing voltage in one direction, and "saturates" at a low value with increasing voltage in the other direction.*

sistance in one direction and a low resistance in the other. Figure 45 makes clear why the p-n junction is called *nonohmic.*

Notice also why the p-n junction is called a *rectifier*, the name received by any device that converts an alternating current into a direct current. Anything connected to a source of alternating current feels an alternating voltage – a voltage that reverses direction in rapid alternation. But, when the p-n junction is so

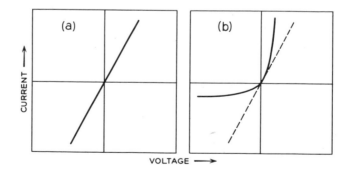

FIGURE 45 – OHM'S LAW *is obeyed when (a) current is proportional to voltage. A conductor, such as the p-n junction, which disobeys that law is called nonohmic (b).*

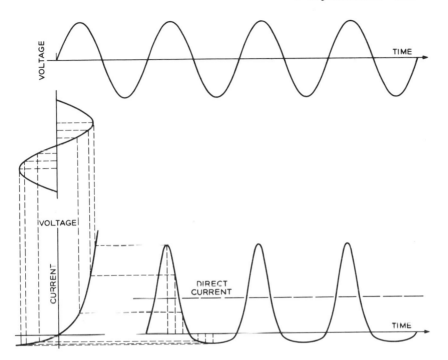

FIGURE 46 – USED AS A RECTIFIER *the p-n junction, energized by an alternating voltage (above), passes a direct current with a superposed ripple (below).*

connected, it passes a large current during half of each alternation, and a very small current during the other half, as Figure 46 shows. The current is like a direct current with a ripple superposed on it. For many purposes — charging storage batteries, for example — this ripple is unimportant. When it is undesirable, the ripple can be ironed out by other electrical devices.

The Solar Cell

Now applying a voltage is not the only way to upset the balance of forward and backward currents across a p-n junction. Illumination of the junction will also upset that balance. Thus such a junction can be used to convert solar power directly into electrical power, a conversion that could be performed hitherto only through a devious chain of plant growth, combustion, and steam turbines, or evaporation, rainfall, and hydroelectric machinery.

The solar cell uses the sun's light directly, not through its heating effect, to produce additional hole-electron pairs on both sides of a junction, without raising the energies of the carriers, as heat would. The additional minority carriers on each side of the junction then diffuse across it—the holes from the n-side going to the p-side, the electrons from the p-side to the n-side. Again, since oppositely charged carriers are diffusing in opposite directions, the two currents are additive. But now they are not compensated by the flows of majority carriers, because the *fractional* increase in the number of majority carriers is small, and the energy of the carriers is not increased.

There are two viewpoints from which you can see how light produces the additional hole-electron pairs. If you prefer to think of light as an electromagnetic wave, you can imagine that the oscillating electrical force of that wave pushes the bonding electrons rapidly back and forth because they bear an electric charge, shaking them hard enough to tear them loose from their bonding positions.

Alternatively you can think of the light as a stream of particles —the little packages of light, called *photons*, that were envisaged by Planck and Einstein, as Chapter 3 described. The energy of each of those particles, you recall, is given by $E = h\nu$, where ν is the frequency of the light. Then you can imagine that photons of suitable energy, striking the bonding electrons, will knock those electrons out of their bonds.

So far, the discussion of junctions has neglected one simple

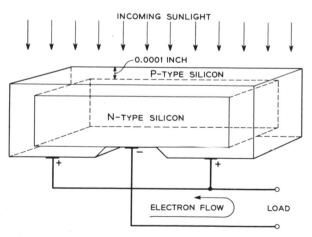

FIGURE 47 – IN THE SOLAR CELL *a p-n junction converts light energy from the sun into electrical energy.*

variable, their size. Looking again at Figure 43, you will recognize the great importance of that variable. The operation of the solar cell depends on the capture, by the junction, of holes diffusing from its n-side. But on that side the mobile electrons greatly outnumber the holes. The odds are heavy that a hole, diffusing toward the brow of a hill, will recombine with a mobile electron before it can escape through the junction. For this reason the only useful holes are those that originate close enough to the junction to reach it before they die. In other words, the light that energizes the solar cell will be wasted if it is absorbed further from the junction than a *diffusion length* – the average distance that a hole diffuses before it recombines with a mobile electron.

The solar cell is therefore arranged so that light will produce the excess minority carriers very close to the junction. As Figure 47 shows, the exposed side of the junction is given a large area, in order to accept as much light as possible, and a thickness of about one ten-thousandth inch, in order to use the accepted light efficiently.

The n-p-n Transistor

We have now met, one by one, all the principles necessary for understanding the simplest type of *transistor*. Briefly rehearsed, they are the following. At a p-n junction there is a charge double layer (Figure 40) that constructs energy hills for the mobile charge carriers. Minority carriers, diffusing to the junction, slide down the hill to the other side, where they soon recombine with their opposites. Majority carriers, diffusing up the hill, are largely turned back by its height. Thus the currents across the junction are normally quite small. The current due to minority carriers is small because those carriers are few; the current due to majority carriers is small because most of them lack adequate energy.

A voltage applied across the junction changes the height of the energy hill. When it is applied in the "forward" direction, it lowers the hill, permitting many more majority carriers to climb it. When the voltage is applied in the "backward" direction, raising the hill still further, it turns back the majority carriers even more effectively, and the current is limited by the small numbers of the minority carriers normally present. But when the number of minority carriers can be increased by some

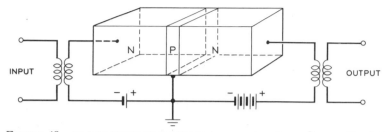

FIGURE 48 – IN THE N-P-N TRANSISTOR *two p-n junctions, disposed back-to-back, amplify electrical signals by converting energy from a battery into signal energy, under the control of an incoming electrical signal.*

means, close enough to the junction to reach it before they recombine, the "backward" current across the junction will increase proportionately.

In the solar cell, light furnishes the means for increasing the number of minority carriers near the junction. In the *junction transistor*, a second junction furnishes those means. The resulting device can accomplish, often to advantage, many of the duties long performed only by vacuum tubes. Transistors contain no filament to be heated, and therefore consume less power and dissipate less heat. They take up less space; they have a longer useful life.

To make an n-p-n transistor, two p-n junctions are introduced back-to-back into a single crystal of germanium or silicon. The three distinguishable regions so produced are connected to sources of constant voltage, to the source of signals to be amplified, and to the electrical circuits that will accept the amplified signals, in the fashion shown in Figure 48.

A battery of low voltage in the input circuit is connected across the n-p junction on the left, with its negative pole to the n-side and its positive pole to the p-side of the junction. Subjected to voltage of that polarity, the junction passes the relatively large current shown at the right side of Figure 44. Furthermore, the varying signal voltage, superposed on the constant voltage of the battery, produces a large variation in the current through the junction. Thus the p-region in the middle of the transistor receives from the left a large input of mobile electrons, varying from instant to instant with the signal voltage.

The battery of high voltage in the output circuit is connected across the p-n junction on the right with its negative pole to the p-side and its positive pole to the n-side of the junction. That junction is therefore normally passing the very small current shown at the left side of Figure 44. But that current is small only because it is limited by the number of electrons that are normally diffusing to the brow of the hill. When the junction at the left floods the p-region with electrons, all those that diffuse to the junction at the right will coast down hill also, just as they do in the solar cell.

Again, therefore, as in the solar cell, the p-region should be no thicker than a diffusion length. If it is so thin that all electrons injected through the junction at the left succeed in reaching the junction at the right, the signal current through the output circuit will be as large as that through the input circuit.

Power Amplification by a Transistor

Why is it worthwhile going to this trouble to produce an output current that can do no better than equal the input current? The answer comes from examining the voltage along with the current. Returning to Figure 44, you see that when a small fluctuation of the signal voltage across the left junction produces a current fluctuation, then the same current fluctuation, passing through the right junction, must be accompanied by a large voltage fluctuation across it. In other words the transistor has amplified the voltage, without losing much current. Since the power dissipated in a circuit is proportional to the current through it times the voltage across it, the transistor has amplified the power available to the output circuit.

You have not got that increased power out of thin air, of course. Where has it come from? It has come from the battery across the junction at the right. The transistor has converted power from that battery into power in the output signal by triggering the battery with the little input signal. In a carefully made transistor the output signal can be given as much as a hundred thousand times the power of the input signal.

The Invention of the Transistor

The pictures of semiconductors and their junctions described in the last two chapters have arisen in important part since the transistor was invented in 1947. Invented, or discovered? In recounting the story of how John Bardeen, Walter Brattain and William Shockley of Bell Telephone Laboratories came to the transistor, some have laid emphasis on the "scientific" motivations, others on the "technological" motivations, that inspired their work. We know from their own statements that they were searching at that time for new knowledge about the behavior of semiconducting solids, and also that they hoped that the new knowledge might assist in constructing a useful device.

Probably it is not wise to insist on making sharp distinctions between such terms as "pure science," "applied science," "device development," and the like. The practical needs of surveying and navigation produced much of the geometry and astronomy that we inherit from the ancients. On the other hand, J. J. Thomson's efforts to identify the electron produced much of the modern technology of electronics. The close interaction between pure curiosity and the urge to develop useful products is implicit in the citation by the Swedish Royal Academy of Sciences, awarding the Nobel Prize in physics for 1956 to the three men jointly "for their researches on semiconductors and their discovery of the transistor effect."

In any case, it is not strange that "their discovery of the transistor effect" exhibited a close parallel with Stephen Gray's discovery of the difference between electrical conductors and nonconductors, described at the beginning of this book. The three men were pursuing an idea about the surfaces of semiconductors that seemed reasonable. And one day, attempting to confirm that idea by experiment, they obtained a wholly unpredicted result.

Problems

1. A molecule of nitrogen gas consists of two atoms of nitrogen. Make a diagram that shows how you would expect the electrons in the two atoms to be shared (Chapter 3) in forming the bond between the atoms.

2. The "Bohr orbit" of lowest energy for an electron in a hydrogen atom is shown in Figure 13.
   (a) Do you expect the time-average "shape" of the hydrogen atom to be a ring?
   (b) Can you think of any mechanical process that is likely to take place in the hydrogen atom which would make the time-average shape a spherical shell?
   (c) Can you think of any phenomenon by which you might distinguish experimentally between a ring generated by an electron moving clockwise around the nucleus from a ring generated by an electron moving in the opposite direction?

3. An electron moving in an orbit about a nucleus has kinetic energy; an electron at rest, a long way off, has none. Then why is energy required to remove an electron from an atom?

4. In copper each atom is surrounded by its immediate neighbors in the way shown in this figure. The metal behaves as if it had one

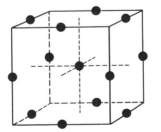

electron per atom available for bonding. What is the electron-deficiency (Chapter 4) in the bonding in metallic copper?

5. In the discussion of conduction by the "free-electron gas" in a metal (Chapter 5), the mobility of the electrons was said to be determined by the frequency of effective collisions of the electrons with the atoms. Why was it unnecessary to consider the collisions of the electrons with one another?

6. When the electrons acquire a drift velocity from the electromotive force, their collisions with the atoms must be a little more violent

in the direction in which the electrons are drifting than their collisions in the reverse direction. In this way the electrons must exert a net time-average force on the atoms of the solid, tending to make the whole solid move in the direction in which the electrons are drifting. If you mounted the solid on some free and frictionless support, would you expect it to move while an electrical current was flowing through it?

7. At very low temperatures the "heat capacity" of a solid (the amount of heat that must be supplied to it to raise its temperature by one degree) increases with the cube of the absolute temperature. If Wien's second guess (Chapter 6) is still valid at low temperatures, how would you expect the conductivity of a metal to vary with temperature at those low temperatures?

8. At some temperature the total number of charge carriers in a piece of pure germanium is twenty billion. If you make a piece of germanium of the same size which contains twenty-one billion arsenic atoms as an impurity, how many charge carriers (Chapter 7) will this piece of germanium have at the same temperature?

9. Even though the arrangement of atoms in diamond is the same as the arrangement in silicon and germanium, thermal energy is inadequate at ordinary temperatures to free any noticeable number of electrons from the electron-pair bonds in diamond. Since visible light is remarkably effective in ejecting electrons from the bonds in silicon and germanium, it is natural to search for a similar effect in diamond. But diamond is transparent to visible light; the light passes right through it without affecting it. In continuing this search, can you guess, by thinking about the mechanism of ejection by light described in Chapter 8, whether you should be more hopeful of infrared light or of ultraviolet light?

10. What is the mobility (Chapter 7) of the free electrons in a metal in terms of their mean free path according to Drude's theory (Chapter 6)?

11. Under what circumstances may the addition of impurities to a semiconductor decrease its conductivity?

Appendix

How To Demonstrate Properties of Conductors and Semiconductors*

Demonstrations of some of the properties and characteristics of materials and devices discussed in this book can be easily presented in the classroom. The setup described here can be used to demonstrate the intrinsic conducting properties of insulators, semiconductors, and conductors, as well as the changes in these properties under the influence of heat and light. The behavior of semiconductor junctions, rectifiers, and solar cells can also be exhibited under various conditions.

In all these demonstrations, the properties of the materials and characteristics of the devices are interpreted from meter readings. These are provided by a 0-to-1 milliammeter connected into the Meter Circuit shown in Figure A1. Three Demonstration Circuits, shown in Figures A2, A3, and A4, can be connected in turn into the Meter Circuit to establish the proper test conditions.

All four of these circuits can be constructed from components available in the school or purchased from local radio supply stores. However, it may be more convenient to use a specially designed classroom device, the Conductivity Demonstration, which combines the four circuits into a single unit. This is available, in both completely assembled and kit form, from the manufacturer listed on page 130.

Many of these demonstrations may also be seen in the motion picture "Brattain on Semiconductor Physics," which was produced by Bell Telephone Laboratories and is available from local Telephone Business Offices.

Building Your Own Demonstration Device

Figures A1 through A4 show all the parts needed to construct your own circuits. These can be mounted and wired in "breadboard" form or on a demonstration panel. The three Demonstration Circuits should be individually mounted so that connections to the Meter Circuit are readily interchangeable. A panel-type, projection-type, or large demonstration meter may be used, provided it is rated at a full-scale deflection of one milliampere.

These samples are used in the demonstrations in this Appendix:

Insulator—a glass rod, 1/8 inch in diameter, 2 inches long

Semiconductor—an n-type germanium rod, 10 ohm-centimeters, measuring 0.08 by 0.04 by 0.8 inch

---

* This section prepared by George R. Frost.

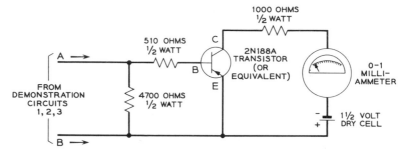

FIGURE A1 – METER CIRCUIT, *which connects at points A and B with Demonstration Circuits 1, 2, and 3.*

Conductor—a coil of pure tungsten wire, 0.006 in diameter, prepared as shown in Figure A5

Rectifier—a glass diode, type 1N34A

Insulator-to-Conductor—a type 41 flashlight bulb and pilot lamp socket, prepared as shown in Figure A6

Photovoltaic Device—a germanium or silicon solar cell

Since some of these may be difficult to obtain locally, complete sets of samples have been assembled; they are available from the supplier listed on page 130.

After the four circuits have been constructed and checked, a fresh dry cell should be installed. Then, to adjust the meter, connect Demonstration Circuit 1 to the Meter Circuit, matching A to A and B to B. Set the meter needle to read zero by means of its zero-set screw, and then disconnect the Demonstration Circuit. Your apparatus is now ready for use.

Suggested Demonstrations

Following are eleven different demonstrations that can be performed in the classroom with the circuits described above and illustrated in Figures A1 through A4. There are also, of course, many others that are possible with this equipment.

(1) Conductivity of an Insulator

Connect Demonstration Circuit 1 to the Meter Circuit. The test clips are now actually "connected" to the air path between them. Since air is an insulator, no deflection of the meter needle is observed. To show that a series circuit exists, short the test clips together with a screw driver or other metal object. Now place the glass rod between the test clips. No reading will be observed on the meter, since glass is an insulator. Record the reading obtained (in this case, zero) for future reference.

(2) Conductivity of a Semiconductor

Remove the glass rod and place the n-type germanium rod between the test clips. A reading will be shown on the meter. This is expected,

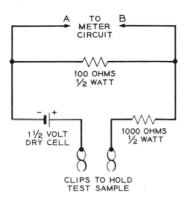

FIGURE A2 – DEMONSTRATION CIRCUIT 1 – *special EMF source for showing conductivity of conductors, semiconductors, insulators, and rectifiers.*

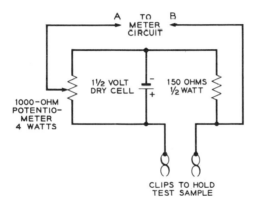

FIGURE A3 – DEMONSTRATION CIRCUIT 2 – *bridge circuit for demonstrating positive and negative temperature coefficient, photoconductivity.*

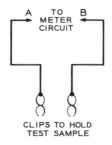

FIGURE A4 – DEMONSTRATION CIRCUIT 3 – *direct circuit for demonstrating thermovoltaic and photovoltaic effects.*

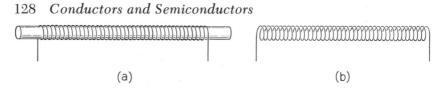

(a)   (b)

FIGURE A5 – METALLIC CONDUCTOR SAMPLE *is prepared by (a) winding 50 turns of tungsten wire closely on a glass rod one-eighth inch in diameter and then (b) slipping the wire carefully off the rod.*

since germanium is a semiconductor. Record the name of the material and reading on the meter for future reference.

(3) Conductivity of a Conductor

Remove the germanium rod and connect the ends of the tungsten wire coil to the test clips. Full deflection of the meter needle will be observed, since the metal tungsten is a conductor. Record this reading also. A comparison between the conductivity of the three sample materials can now be made by means of the recorded readings. Keep in mind the differences in conductivity caused by the differences in physical size of the samples, as discussed in Chapter 1. Other samples of insulators, conductors, and semiconductors may also be tested and their reading recorded and compared.

(4) Positive Temperature Coefficient of Resistance

Disconnect Demonstration Circuit 1 from the Meter Circuit and connect Demonstration Circuit 2. A Wheatstone bridge circuit is now set up that will indicate very small changes in conductivity. Connect the coil of tungsten wire to the test clips. By means of the potentiometer, adjust the meter to the reading that you obtained for tungsten wire in Demonstration 3 above. (If the reading previously obtained was over 10, set the meter to read about 9.) Heat the tungsten wire with a match, candle, or bunsen burner. Note that the meter reading decreases, indicating a reduction of current. Since conductance is the reciprocal of resistance, the lowered meter reading indicates an *increase* in resistance. Metal conductors exhibit this positive temperature coefficient of resistance (see Chapter 7).

(5) Negative Temperature Coefficient of Resistance

Replace the tungsten wire with the germanium rod. Adjust the potentiometer to obtain the reading you recorded in Demonstration 2 above. Heat the germanium near the center with a match or candle. Note that the meter reading now increases, indicating a *decrease* in resistance, since semiconductors exhibit a negative temperature coefficient of resistance (see Chapter 7).

(6) Photoconductivity

Now shine a bright light (such as a 100-watt spotlight) directly on the

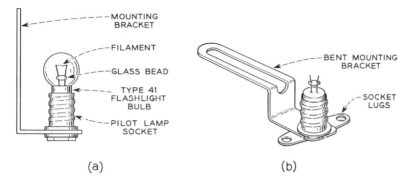

FIGURE A6 – GLASS BEAD *is obtained for use in Demonstration 7 from a type 41 flashlight bulb. Screw the bulb securely into a pilot lamp socket, as in (a), and carefully crush the glass bulb between the jaws of a vice to expose the glass bead. Then remove the filament just above the bead, bend the mounting bracket so that it can be used as a handle, as shown in (b), and connect test clips to the socket lugs.*

germanium rod. Note again that the meter reading increases. But in this case light energy absorbed by the semiconductor, rather than heat energy, is responsible for the change in conductivity of the material.

(7) Insulator-to-Conductor

Prepare a flashlight bulb and pilot lamp socket as shown in Figure A6, and place the lugs in the test clips. The glass bead separating the two filament leads in the prepared bulb is an insulator, so no reading will be indicated on the meter. Now heat the glass bead with a cigarette lighter, candle, or bunsen burner. Note that a reading is obtained on the meter, showing that the concentrated application of heat can change the insulator, glass, into a conductor.

(8) Thermovoltaic Effect at a p-n Junction

Replace Demonstration Circuit 2 with Demonstration Circuit 3, which sets up a direct connection to the Meter Circuit. With this circuit, the behavior of junctions between materials can be studied. Place the germanium rod in the test clips. Use a candle, cigarette lighter, or bunsen burner to heat the junction formed by one clip and the rod. Note that a reading is obtained on the meter. (If the meter deflects in the wrong direction, allow the junction to cool and then heat the other junction.) This indicates that a current is produced when one junction is heated and the other kept cool (see Chapter 8).

(9) Photovoltaic Effect – Solar Cell

Remove the germanium rod and connect the solar cell to the test clips. Shine a bright light on the cell, and note that the meter indicates that a current is being generated, as discussed in Chapter 8. (If the meter deflects in the wrong direction, reverse the solar cell leads.)

(10) Photovoltaic Effect – Diode
Repeat this demonstration using the 1N34A diode in place of the solar cell.

(11) p-n Junction as a Rectifier
The rectifying properties of a p-n junction, described in Chapter 8, can be demonstrated by replacing Demonstration Circuit 3 with Demonstration Circuit 1. Connect the diode to the clips, first in one direction, then in the other. Note the difference in current readings.

✿   ✿   ✿

CONDUCTIVITY DEMONSTRATION DEVICE
As mentioned above, a specially designed classroom demonstration has been developed that combines all four of the circuits described on these pages. The Meter Circuit is mounted on an inclined display panel and includes a large milliammeter and convenient test clips. The three Demonstration Circuits make use of printed circuits and are separately mounted on boards that can be easily slipped onto the display panel. A separate package includes all the samples listed on pages 125 and 126.

This material is available from:
North Hills Electronics
Alexander Place
Glen Cove, New York
Prices:

Completely assembled (including samples):	$58.00
In kit form (without samples):	$49.00
Package of samples:	$ 7.00

All prices include postage and are subject to change without notice

The Author

Alan Holden was born in New York City, graduated from Montclair, New Jersey, High School, and received his S.B. degree from Harvard College in 1925. That same year, he came to work at Bell Telephone Laboratories, where he has worked ever since. He has been engaged in research in many branches of chemistry and physics, including artificial piezoelectric materials, methods for growing large single crystals, and spectroscopy in the microwave region.

Mr. Holden has worked extensively with the Physical Science Study Committee in its efforts to revise the high school physics curriculum. In this capacity, he prepared two movies, "Crystals" and "Matter Waves," that have been widely shown in high schools throughout the country. He is also the co-author of "Crystals and Crystal Growing" published by Doubleday and Co. as part of its Anchor Science Series.

During the academic year 1961-1962 Mr. Holden was visiting Professor in the Physics Department of Massachusetts Institute of Technology.

Index of Names